Awards 37

Nimrod International Journal

Awards 37

ISBN: 978-0-9860178-6-5 ISSN: 0029-053X
Volume 59, Number 1
Fall/Winter 2015

THE UNIVERSITY OF TULSA — TULSA, OKLAHOMA

Editorial Board

Advisory Board

ACKNOWLEDGEMENTS

This issue of *Nimrod* is funded by donations, subscriptions, and sales. *Nimrod* and The University of Tulsa acknowledge with gratitude the many individuals and organizations that support *Nimrod*'s publication, annual prize, and outreach programs: *Nimrod*'s Advisory and Editorial Boards; and *Nimrod*'s Angels, Benefactors, Donors, and Patrons.

ANGEL ($1,000+)	Ellen & Stephen Adelson, George Krumme, Susan and Robert Mase, Office of Institutional Advancement at The University of Tulsa, Francine Ringold, Ann Daniel Stone, Randi and Fred Wightman, The John Steele Zink Foundation
BENEFACTOR ($500+)	Stephani Franklin, Cynthia Gustavson, The Ruth K. Nelson Trust, Sandra and Dobie Langenkamp, Lisa Ransom and David Flesher, Jane Wiseman
DONOR ($100+)	Teresa and Alex Adwan, Ann Alspaugh, Diane Burton, Katherine and John Coyle, Ivy Dempsey, Patricia Eaton, Marion and William Elson, Sherri and Stuart Goodall, Ellen Hartman, Frank X. Henke III, Nancy and William Hermann, Linda Jennings, Elizabeth and Sam Joyner, The Kerr Foundation, Inc., Marjorie and David Kroll, Robert LaFortune, Roberta Marder, Geraldine McLoud, Catherine Gammie Nielsen, Lynne Novack, Donna O'Rourke, Pamela Pearce, Joan and Harry Seay, Diane and James Seebass, TD Design, Fran and Bruce Tibbetts, Marlene Wetzel, Penny Williams, Josephine Winter, Maria and Yevgeny Yevtushenko, Rachel Zebrowski
PATRON ($25+)	Margaret and Charles Audrain, Denise Brice, John Coward, Kim Doenges, Linda and William Epperson, William Flynn, Inge Kahn, William Livingston, Constance Murray, Joshua Parish, Thomas Payne, Katie and Ron Petrikin, Krista and John Waldron, Ann Watson, Manuel Watts

Table of Contents

Editor's Note:

Welcome to *Awards 37*! In these pages, a gem cutter searches for the signs of flaws hidden in the human soul, while a prescribed burn-setter for the Forestry Service tries to come to terms with the effects of a fire that helped destroy her marriage. A blueprint for the infinite takes us to strange and celestial heights, and the small details of a Muslim family's life resonate with vibrancy and clarity. These are the premises behind the winning stories and poems from this year's *Nimrod* Literary Awards, and these remarkable works and more await you in this, our 37th Annual Awards publication.

Each year, our editors read the hundreds of manuscripts sent for The Katherine Anne Porter Prize for Fiction and The Pablo Neruda Prize for Poetry and, after often lively debate, carefully select our finalists. The finalists are then sent to the final judges, who award first and second prizes, as well as honorable mentions. This year, we were thrilled to have Karen Russell, Pulitzer-Prize finalist and author of *Swamplandia!,* serve as our fiction judge and Tina Chang, Brooklyn Poet Laureate and author of *Of Gods and Strangers,* as our poetry judge. They did the tough work of selecting J. Duncan Wiley and Emily Wortman-Wunder as our first- and second-prize fiction winners and Heather Altfeld and Leila Chatti as our first- and second-prize poetry winners. All four of our winners offer work that is diverse and fascinating, moving from the cosmic to the personal, from the burdens of loneliness to the solace of friendship.

In addition to our winners, we are proud to feature the work of our Awards honorable mentions, finalists, and semi-finalists, as well as work accepted throughout the year. As with our winners, the pieces here are by turns enchanting and disquieting, but always challenging and compelling. Katharyn Howd Machan explores the dark side of fairy tales in the poem "My Beast," while Michelle Collins Anderson uses the Harry Potter novels to frame her story about the ways a family confronts the approaching death of a husband and father. Josephine Yu, Catherine Freeling, and Jennifer Clark all employ sly humor in their poems, "Middle Class Love Song," "In Which I Praise My Right Foot," and "Searching," using that humor to enliven and enrich. Stephanie Carpenter considers what is real and not real in "The Sweeper," a story that asks us to imagine what might happen if words began disappearing—or were taken—from the English language, and Susanne Kort, Lorna Crozier, and Zane Kokter all depict loss in moving, deliberate language that distills the personal into the universal.

We are also especially pleased to publish a poem by the late Charlotte Stewart, *Nimrod*'s beloved former Associate Editor, and very excited to end this issue with work by former U.S. Poet Laureate Ted Kooser.

We are pleased to present these and 35 other works of fiction and poetry. Thank you for joining us as we begin our fifty-ninth year of discovery.

Eleanor Leonne Bennett, *Blurred,* photograph

The Nimrod Literary Awards
The Pablo Neruda Prize for Poetry

First Prize
Heather Altfeld

Blueprint for the Infinite

The existence of the infinite
is in every respect impossible.
—Maimonides

Here is pretty much how things happen.
Out in the snow, a figure
waddles his way up the hill
and the freezing wind blows so hard
that the bundle we know as him
smashes into a rock.
One dizzy sparrow grazes the windshield of a Camry
halfway back from Thanksgiving in Des Moines,
and a hundred-and-ninety-two cars trailing behind on black ice
skitter and crash outside Battle Creek.
Someone calls an ambulance,
someone else calls the newspaper;
somewhere in the rubble of the wreckage
someone dies so quickly that their life ends
before the telephone is answered.
Somewhere the sparrow
will be worshipped as a god.

In the Alps, strange winds gather
and glitter down the mountainside,
lathering the slush and crushing the lupine,
hurling the bees against the rocks.
The minds of the people who live in the valley
begin to burn—Alpine wind, *Foehn,*
and on the third day of wind the little villages
reached only by gondola
are hives of underwashed Alpsters
frying the mice they find behind their beds.

When the ether dome was in full swing
and anesthesia was still a strange dream
forgotten by morning, patients threw themselves
from the rooftops of buildings
to avoid the knife, hoping the firmament
would catch and save them. Or they endured
six men holding them down

as the sound of their old bones
fell to the floor.
And after defending the dancing of Jews
in the ancient city of Alexandria,
Hypatia was killed by a crowd with oyster shells
and shards of pottery—
they scooped up her heart
on fragments that once held bread and sweets and pearls.

In Polish the metaphor for getting ready to die
is that you are "packing up for your journey."
Do you lie awake at night,
wondering what to take on your departure?
The whole universe, says Maimonides,
is composed of substance and accidents.
And the heart, he tells us,
is in constant motion, ruling
over the other members and communicates to them
through its own pulsations. If for one instant
the beating of the heart is interrupted,
man dies, and all of his motions and powers
come to an end. In a like manner,
would the whole universe perish
and everything therein cease to exist
if the spheres were to come to a standstill?

So if the wind gets an idea
about disassembling us, particle
by particle, carrying us off
and inheriting our ions
as it pearls down from the mountaintops,
should we pack a rucksack and wait for a ride

or take shelter in the bank of fog by the river
or cover ourselves with dry leaves
and play dead? *Stop, heart,*
call the waves on the radio,
transmitting messages from the infinite.
Stop the luminous machinery,
the fantastical device of the bronchi.
Let the frozen script of the earth
find you and take you to bed.
Let the sheets of grass
and the pillow of moss
cover you sweetly.
Let the walls of your tomb
be painted with daffodils.
When they come to check for your breath,
whisper that you are already packed.
Close your ventricles and then your eyes.
When they try to flog you with canes
or take bellows to your lungs
to pump them full of life,

or when they lift your heart
from the socket of the body
and slide it into a cool dish,

just remember the impossible length of night
and the gravity of darkness as it pulls
its long slow chains across the sky.
Let them sigh as your last breath
curls back into the cold furnace of the ribs.
Farewell, sweet pea. Farewell false dawn,
and tea that never wakens.
When the room is quiet again,
and the ether of the sky has dissipated,

you can slough off your body
and those messy shards. Walk around,
feel your new ribs wiggle. Your vanishing
is only the beginning of the infinite.

Two Pockets

What is it that can penetrate
the pliant human heart? Rabbi Akiva asked,
just weeks or months before being laid out
on a coffin-sized stone, interrogated
by Tyrannus Rufus, whose name speaks
for itself, and flayed with an iron comb,
which, by all accounts, is described as
"similar to a miniature garden-rake,
only stronger," heated directly in a fire,
and pulled across the skin while the victim is still alive.
This particular victim, who asked the above question about the human heart—
his was still beating as they flayed him, and his mouth
was still moving, mouthing the words to the one prayer
that calls every Jew to God, or is supposed to,
if it is working properly, and if God is working properly,
doing his job, sewing little crowns to the letters of the Torah
in Akiva's name—as he looked into their faces,
those Levantine faces, turned up to the light
that they thought for a while was theirs.

I'm not talking about what is true,
I'm talking about what is remembered.
What is true in the small history of skin reveals
that a lot of it can be flayed while your heart is still alive
and while your lips are still singing in praise
and while your followers, 24,000 of them,
wait outside for the spectacle that is your piety
as a rapt and genuine audience to your pain.
Arendt has it at least partially right, banality

is sleeping with a newspaper over your head
in a train car stopped right next to a train car.
And the parents who send their children out into the world
with *I am but dust and ashes* written on a slip of paper
folded and carried in a pocket over the heart
have it partially right, the humble know
humility needs a compass, the smug and the righteous
a map. What is remembered: Being a child

during the era of dust and ashes.
The parents of what is called the silent generation—
and by this I think it is meant that they lay silent
because they didn't know what else to do—met the toils
and injustices of the world
with the twentieth century's favorite
barometer of pain, the great trump card of parenting,
the grand dismiss. *At least*
you are not on the train. The way parents
in Akiva's era must have said to their young *kippot,*
At least you are not being flayed alive
with iron combs. What is remembered.
This tactic works on everything
from the injustices of weeding in midsummer
to the long hours of sadness and nothing
endured in the life of a child
to the minute of grief you are allowed to feel
just before and just after a death.
This is not what is true, but what is remembered.

The first cry we shriek upon being born
translates to something like this:
For my sake the world is created! This is what the Talmud
tells us must be on the other slip of paper
in the other pocket worn over the other heart,
it is how we enter this place,
stomping at the mothers and the fathers
as is the will and right of being alive.
Then the space between stomps is explained
as a curl of smoke made of children's bones and little teeth,
and the sky smallens and shuts with the velocity of a clam.
This world is revealed to us in tiny pieces

that make no apparent sense, parcels the size of sand
and anti-sand, rubbed and worried
by the rabbis and the scientists,
who daven with Talmudic fury over every particle.
Is it true? Does it bear scrutiny?
The peas on the plate that don't want to be eaten,
the mothers parting our hair, the laws against firecrackers,

sodomy, chain-smoking in public,
the disappearance of bees and of love—
all of it bears scrutiny, all of it relentlessly bantered
on the *bima* and in the laboratories until the loudest cry
to the sky wins. Here is what is true:

Goebbels announced with pride in the newspapers
during the summer of 1937 that *The Fuhrer is very happy.*
He had visited the Kunstmuseum,
where the opposite of degenerate paintings
were hung with the greatest of care.
No pockets at all on the shirts
or above the hearts,
just the black sorcery of emptiness
hung with more emptiness
hanging next to a cleanliness
born to rinse the world, bottled and soldered
in the space where the heart should be. *Tyrannus Rufus.*
It sounds like Latin for "he who would kill even the dead."
Had you flayed them alive,

their blood would run clear and glad
as the grease of a *dybbuk*,
their bones malformed by the pressures
that live beneath the earth, seizing the stones
with the long slow violence that is matter.
I'm not talking about what is remembered now,
I am talking about what is true. In this cold world
spiraling with loss and fossils
where humans get boiled like soups,
there is always another sadness
to bear and endure. To the children
who fall to us like rain,

to the sea, to the stars, to the holy ozone
that screams in the wind, to scrutiny,
which has failed us miserably, as scrutiny so often does,
here are the pockets to sew over your heart.
And then, do as you will. In the end,
Akiva told his students, *All my life I was worried*

about the verse in the Shema, "with all my soul,"
and I wondered if I would be able to fulfill its command.
And now that I am finally able to fulfill it,
I should not? Even in the end it was a question.
His body was taken by Elijah to Caesarea,
on a night, we are told, bright as day,
to a cavern where only a book,
a bed, a table, a chair, and a lamp waited.
His body was left on the bed. When Elijah departed,
the cavern sealed of its own accord
and was never found again.
We have only what is remembered.
We can only carry the chairs
and the children on our backs
and the notes in our pockets
and the light that for now we can claim
as ours.

The Nimrod Literary Awards

The Katherine Anne Porter Prize for Fiction

First Prize

J. Duncan Wiley

Inclusions

One of those nights when the sky ran deep and the cosmos was flung from horizon to horizon like handfuls of diamond sand, Mae's grandfather took her tiny fingers in his and pointed upward, saying, "It looks big, sweetheart. But remember, nothing's forever. Even stars die."

"They do?" Something in her voice must have trembled because her grandfather laughed and hugged her close.

"Don't you worry." He lowered his voice to a whisper, leaned in so that his whiskery lips scratched her ear. "Nothing's lost. Those old stars spark and flare and fall to earth. And that's where we come in." He dug in his shirt pocket and after a moment produced something between his thumb and index finger, waving it once like a magician before bringing it to rest before her eyes. The object was dark, the size of a grape, though it seemed unlikely her grandfather would carry a grape over his heart. He unfolded her hand and placed it carefully on her upturned palm. "This," he told her, "is a fossil star." It sat with a pleasant weight, still radiating his body heat.

At first she didn't know what to do. If she should drop it in this field, it would be swallowed in the long grass, lost forever. She held her breath and stood statue-still, her hand out as though presenting the dead star on an invisible platter. Just as she was starting to panic with responsibility, she saw merriment in her grandfather's eyes. He bumped her shoulder, chased off her trepidation with a playful quirk of his eyebrows. She inhaled. Began to relax. Finally bent her neck to get a better look. The star was hard and smooth. She saw now that it wasn't as perfectly shaped as a grape. One side was fatter than the other, its surface scarred and dimpled. As she turned her hand to examine it from other angles, something deep inside caught the moonlight and shimmered, glowing with intense blue life.

Before she could really lose herself in that mysterious glow, her grandfather interrupted by mussing her hair. "It's something you have to understand, Mae. Most people just get by on this earth. They pick a trade, settle into some kind of work, do whatever they can to make ends meet. Doctors, lawyers, garbage men—it's all the same." Here he crouched, plucking the star from her hand as he settled onto his heels. Before she could protest, he'd wrapped it in a handkerchief and returned it to her. "But that isn't our lot. We're different, you and me. We have a purpose." He looked long and hard into her face.

Mae gripped the handkerchief, unsure if she was supposed to answer.

"We're here to find those old stars," he continued. "And when we do, we give them back their fire."

This was a moment that had settled upon Mae like a fine dust, almost unnoticed when it first coated the skin of her being. But long after she discovered that her grandfather's stars were not stars at all, the fairytale clung to her. All through her adolescence and five semesters of college, through a failed marriage, a child, and another failed marriage—for nearly all her life—she had continued to think of herself as a bearer of celestial fire. And then one day she found herself in the shop standing over a steel and glass display case filled with nothing more remarkable than sparkling rocks.

It was a Saturday in late spring, the time of year when her business yawned and stretched, waking to the busy season that hovered just around the corner. Traffic through the shop had been sporadic, mostly regulars who lived in Helena and came out several times a summer with the hope of striking it rich. They laughed and chatted and pretended familiarity with her. Their faces gleamed with pleasantries. More than one asked if she had found the next Queen Marie or Logan Sapphire yet. Then they bought a bag or two of gravel and left. She watched their backs as they shouldered through the door, wished they would leave more quickly.

By the time Dan came in with the mail, she had been more than an hour without a customer and was beginning to allow herself the hope that she'd seen the last of them for the day. "Hey, Mae." Dan gave her his usual understated wave.

She returned the greeting.

He slid the bundle of envelopes across the countertop. Neither a large nor a small man, not chiseled or particularly strong in appearance, he conveyed an overall impression of rounded edges and a lack of corners. But he had a solid, dependable presence. Offhand she couldn't remember exactly how long ago she had hired him to oversee the Anvil Bar Mine. Sometimes it seemed he'd always been around. While she flipped through the mail, he half-leaned, half-sat against the counter, hands in the pockets of his dun jacket, gaze directed toward the toes of his boots.

For the most part it was the standard mix: junk, bank statements, bills. She pulled out a packet from the faceting service and set it aside. She also pulled out a letter with her son's name on the return address line and, below that, an inky red stamp proclaiming, "This was mailed by an inmate confined at a Washington State Department of Corrections facility. Its contents are uncensored." Thin and almost weightless, it couldn't have contained more than a page or two of her son's cramped handwriting. She shuffled it to the bottom of the pile.

"Well." Dan pushed himself off the counter.

Something in the way he paused made Mae fear she was about to hear yet another aphorism meant to pick up her spirits. But all he said was, "Guess I'd better shove off," and then he was through the door and gone.

She had never had romantic feelings toward Dan, but in that moment, she loved him. Loved that he spoke little and kept his thoughts to himself. Loved that, unlike everyone else she knew, he didn't try to distract her or bury her in clouds of sympathy and manufactured cheerfulness.

The building breathed, filling her nostrils with the scent of old unfinished wood. Now that she was alone, she retrieved the envelope with her son's name on it. Such a slight thing. After letting it linger a moment in her hand, she stuck it with the others, all unopened, way back in the dark part of the drawer beneath the counter. The drawer shut with a soft click.

She turned her attention to the packet from the faceting service, slitting its top with a pair of scissors. When it was upended, five faceted stones spilled from its mouth, each in its own miniature ziplock bag, plinking one after another onto the glass of the display case. Four were a matched set: one carat each, step cut, a nice medium blue. Pretty enough, but nothing special. The true gem was the fifth stone, a seven-point-three-carat Portuguese round that shone brilliant orange. She removed it from its bag and placed it on the bare glass. Using her fingertip, she rolled it on its pavilion, watching the light from the display case below dance and refract through its crown. Once, such a sight would have filled her with a near religious reverence. Even now, though she no longer felt she was brushing against the edge of some transcendent mystery, she couldn't help but admire the stone's beauty and the skill that went into cutting and polishing it. Still, it wasn't on a par with her grandfather's work. In his time he had turned out wonders. A six-hundred-forty-two-carat topaz he'd cut was on display at the Smithsonian, noted for both the flawlessness of the gem and the perfection of his artistry.

As she stood there, in the building that had once been her grandfather's combined workshop and toolshed—stood, in fact, almost on the exact spot where he had sat so many hours bent over his jamb-peg lap—Mae reflected that she must now be close to the same age he had been when he took her out into that moonlit field all those decades ago and placed a raw sapphire in her hand.

She scooped up the five new stones, bent to unlock the display case door and slide it to one side. The case was six feet wide and three feet tall, standard jewelry counter stuff. Of all the items in the shop, it was the most conspicuously modern. Inside it had two glass shelves plus an opaque base. On the top shelf sat the green and blue sapphires, the colors most common to the placer gravel deposits beneath her land, ranging in hue from the palest periwinkle to the deepest cobalt. The shelf below held the less common yellows and pinks, the rare oranges, a single ruby. Also on the second shelf were the garnets, the topazes, and five gold nuggets. The very bottom she used for purely decorative purposes. It was covered with a dark, gleaming bed of hematite pieces upon which rested two of her grandfather's dopsticks, partially faceted sapphires still cemented to their ends. They were the last two stones he'd been working on.

While she was in the middle of rearranging the display to create space for the new pieces, she heard the crunch of tires pulling up in the dirt lot outside, followed by the slam of car doors. A family of four filed into the shop, spreading themselves amongst the little merchandise she stocked. The father was drawn to the rough-hewn shelves on one wall that held mesh screens, gold pans, books about the geology of Montana. The mother, like most women, went straight to the display case. The two boys—maybe eight and ten—rifled through the single rack of t-shirts and twirled the spinner filled with postcards before joining their mother at the case where, one to either side of her, they pressed their foreheads and fingertips against the glass.

"Isn't this a quaint little place," the father said, running his hand along one of the plank shelves.

The mother peered at the gemstones. "Mmmm," she said.

They were young parents, slender, clad in close-fitting outdoorsy gear and designer sunglasses. A ridiculous number of carabineers hung from their belt loops and camera straps. They were the kind of people, Mae thought, who probably ran marathons for fun on weekends. Their boys were blond and wore their hair like it had been arranged by a magazine photographer to appear windblown. In fact, the whole family could have stepped out of an advertisement for mountain bikes or camping equipment.

The father joined the rest of his family near the counter just as the boys were beginning to argue over which of them would find the biggest sapphire. Neither parent stepped in to quell the squabble. "You gotta love their enthusiasm," the father grinned. "Joey. Hey, Joey. Tell the lady about the opal you found at Spencer."

Neither boy responded. Their argument escalated to pushes and shoves.

"Guess we'd better get them out to the sapphire mine before they break something," the father laughed, pulling out his wallet.

Mae glanced at the clock over the door. She wanted to tell this man to take his brats away and never come back. She wanted to tell him that no matter how deeply he looked into his sons' eyes, there were seeds in their brains that would remain invisible until they bloomed into adulthood. At the very least she wanted to tell him that she was closing early today and that he was out of luck.

But she said none of that. Instead she said, "I close shop in two hours, so you'll have to be quick about it."

* * *

Mae's own son, Bentley, was serving his first month of a life sentence. A long list of convictions had been read at the end of the trial. She couldn't remember them all, much less the various degrees of offense. What stuck out in her memory was this: seven counts of rape, possession of a chemical used to drug the women, and filming the women without their consent. There was no doubt about his guilt. The evidence against him was both plentiful and overwhelming. The jury had returned with a verdict in what seemed a matter of minutes. Yet for all the legal certainty surrounding the case, Mae was left with nothing but questions—an unchartable, ever expanding galaxy of them.

After the trial, an image of Bentley as a child would find her at odd moments of the day, peeking around the corners of her routines. She couldn't shake it. She might be driving into town, or filling orders her customers placed online, or talking to Dan about mine operations, and suddenly she would be remembering that disproportioned boy with the undersized body and the overlarge head, eyes turned round and owlish by a pair of glasses with thick lenses. It was an unfortunate appearance, but it fit. From an early age Bentley had been more interested in keeping ant farms and growing sugar crystals than he had been in fishing and playing catch. Most of the time he spent outdoors was devoted to gathering leaves and flowers of various plants, which he pressed between the pages of the dictionary, the world atlas, any volume of size he could reach. Lifting a book in their house was likely to result in a shower of flaking plant matter.

Bentley's father had worried they were raising a sissy. In addition to his bookish pursuits, Bentley was given to bouts of crying. He cried when other children teased him at school; he cried at the sight of a dead raccoon beside the road; he cried after the Discovery Channel aired a show about dwindling rainforests. "That kid cries," his father had said, "if his Rice Krispies don't snap, crackle, and pop just right. We've got to toughen him up, or the world will chew him to pulp." And yet, there grown Bentley had sat in the courtroom, straight-backed, sharp-jawed, awful, the last person in need of hardening.

Mae picked through memories of her son's boyhood, peering into them the way her grandfather had peered into facet rough, looking for fractures and inclusions that might ruin the finished product. Yet no matter how many memories she held to the light, turning them this way and that, she found no serious flaws, no red flags, no smoking guns, nothing that explained how her sensitive boy with dark eyes could grow into a man capable of such crimes. She and his father had divorced, but the split wasn't bitter, and it hadn't seemed to affect Bentley much anyway. He had continued to do well in school. He became more outgoing and accumulated friends. Eventually he went on to earn two degrees in botany and take a job with a nonprofit in Seattle where he worked to preserve the ecosystems of the Pacific Northwest. In his spare time he volunteered in community outreach programs at local museums.

It simply didn't make sense.

Her friends took her out for breakfast, for dinner, for drinks. It's not nature versus nurture, they told her during these outings. It's nature *and* nurture, in equal parts. There were some things, they told her, that couldn't be anticipated, couldn't be curbed. It wasn't her fault. It was nobody's fault. Some things just were.

Now letters from Bentley arrived several times a week in the mail. She had read the first two. In them he wrote about books he borrowed from the prison library and books he wished the library owned. He described his quest to start an heirloom vegetable garden under the auspices of the Sustainability in Prisons Project. He joked about his cravings for a slice of huckleberry pie. In both letters he sounded so much like the Bentley she knew, so exactly like her son, that waves of dizziness and nausea washed over her. How could her boy and the monster that had been revealed in the courtroom be the same person? How could they be? When the next letter came, she held it pinched between her fingers until her entire hand trembled. Finally, unable to open it, she had consigned it to the drawer. Only gradually did the tightness in her chest loosen.

* * *

Open to the sky, the Anvil Bar Mine sat on the bluffs above Hauser Lake. The mine itself was not impressive, a relatively shallow excavation as these things went, running between twenty and thirty feet from the surface to the pay level and spanning about three-hundred-by-one-hundred feet. In its bottom waited a pair of waist-high rocker boxes and a handful of shovels and pickaxes. It was dusty and dry and looked like an ordinary gravel pit. More than once Mae had heard first-timers standing on its lip whisper to their companions, "That's it?" But for all the awe it failed to inspire, the mine was framed by stunning vistas. To one side, warm grassy expanses swept off toward Helena. To the other, across the glittering waters of Hauser Lake, the Big Belt Mountains hunkered, chewing at the skyline. Sometimes Mae came out here to be alone. To sit and to breathe and to remember the time in her youth when the world had seemed without limits.

It was maybe a two-minute drive from the shop. Mae led the way in her truck, parked well away from the mine's edge when they got there. The family followed suit. Everyone exited their vehicles.

"Would you look at that," the father said, facing the Big Belts.

The mother came around the car to share his view. After a moment she said, "Kids, get the camera. I want some pictures of you just there."

Once the mother had photographed the boys in a number of poses and had filled probably half their camera's memory, Mae led the family down into the mine. They took the graded ramp that Dan used for the loader and other machinery. Under his arms the father carried two five-gallon buckets for collecting the material they mined. Usually, as she walked down the ramp with customers, Mae talked about how the Missouri River had carved this valley, depositing gem-rich gravel bars along its banks thousands of years before Hauser Lake was created by a dam. Today, however, she said none of this. To this family she said only, "Being heavy, gemstones tend to settle low in the deposits. You're most likely to find sapphires close to bedrock." The boys were already out of earshot, having raced down the ramp, skidding now and then on loose dirt before ping-ponging out into the flat mine bed.

This particular quarry was not the first belonging to the Anvil Bar Mine. The deposits her grandfather had mined had long since been reclaimed, filled in and planted over with native vegetation, just as this one would be before another was dug further along the gravel bar. When Mae and the parents reached the bottom, she took them across to the opposite edge where Dan had removed the overburden, leaving a shelf of sediment that stood four-and-a-half feet off the mine's floor. The boys, who had rejoined the group, had to jump to see over it. "This is the gravel deposit," she told the family. "What you want to do is dig down from the top, running every shovelful through the rocker boxes as you go." The rocker boxes were wooden frames that sat on four legs, each with a hinged cradle that held two mesh screens, one atop the other with a few inches between. She demonstrated how to sift gravel through the devices, swinging their cradles back and forth to separate out material that was either too big or too small. "Once you've run it through the rockers, you'll want to save everything that's left in the screens."

The father squatted, filled his palm with loose gravel. With the index finger of his other hand he sorted through it. "Looks like rocks to me. How do we tell if there are any sapphires in there?"

"You won't know till you get the gravel home and get it washed," Mae said. "Everything comes out of the ground covered in dirt."

The younger boy ran up to her with a piece of milky quartz. "Is this a sapphire?"

"No," she told him. "Sapphires are glassy. They'll be real clear."

The older boy held up a slightly less milky piece of quartz. "What about this? Is this a sapphire?"

"No. Gemstones radiate light," she said. "Look for something that gathers light and holds it."

The boys ran off to search elsewhere around the pit, their faces flushed and feverish. She didn't care if they understood what she meant about the light. They scooted from one pile of detritus to the next, yelling stories to one another about the treasures that must surely be lying just inches away.

The mother stood with one hand on her hip, watched as her boys' search gradually transformed into a game of tag. "You say most of the sapphires are at the bottom of the deposit?"

Mae gave her a close look. "They're scattered all through the gravel bar," she answered. "You want to dig top to bottom so you don't miss anything. There are no shortcuts. You have to go through all the material to get what you're after. Cutting corners will get you nothing but trouble."

The mother didn't reply. She gazed off toward her boys, who were now beginning to throw rocks at each other. After a moment she waved her hand as though in dismissal.

Mae was happy to leave these fools be. She climbed the earthen ramp out of the mine, pausing near the top to watch the family begin their digging. The father had picked up a shovel and was pointing with it, trying to direct his family's efforts. The others seemed to be ignoring him. The mother hadn't moved from her place, still stood with one hand on her hip as though she was above it all, and the boys hadn't yet given up on running and throwing rocks and shouting.

Lately Mae had taken to wishing ill on people. She saw the postman and thought, *I hope you get dog bit*. She saw a young mother playing slots at Frontier Pies and thought, *I hope you lose every last thing to your name*. She saw her own face in the mirror, hiding behind wrinkles and sagging flesh, and she thought, *I hope the wolves get you. I hope a grizzly tears you limb from limb and leaves your bones to bleach in the sun*. Mae didn't seriously want any of this. Every time one of these thoughts came to her unbidden, it was followed by a tingle of shame on the back of her neck. Yet still the thoughts came. She saw this family in her mine, the boys running wild, their behavior unchecked by the parents, and she thought, *I hope your boys shout and fight and hit each other until their noses are bloody. I hope you blame each other for their shortcomings as you age. And I hope you find nothing here. I hope you carry all those pounds of gravel back to your home, only to discover the weight of failure in every worthless pebble.*

⁂ ⁂ ⁂

Mae's grandfather once told her every gemstone was a window that opened onto the universe. This was maybe two years after that night in the field, and she'd been spending regular periods of time in his workshop ever since, observing the process by which he returned the fire to his fossil stars. Of course she knew by then that the stones were really sapphires, but in her mind they still glimmered with the vestiges of sidereal light.

She sat at a right angle to her grandfather, watching a wooden lap spin and spin, polishing the table facet of the stone he held to its surface."What do you mean, window?" she said.

Her grandfather lifted the sapphire off the lap and set it aside, then leaned forward, his elbows on his knees. For a long time he looked into her face, appraising. She stuck her chin out, determined to meet his gaze. Finally he clapped his hands and said, "Okay. I think you're ready." He turned the lap off and pushed himself up from his stool.

Ready? For what? She watched as her grandfather bustled about, cleaning up. After he straightened his tools, he brought over a variety of finished gems on a black velvet tray and handed it to her. Then he turned to rummage through the cupboard where he kept his saws and grinding stones. She peered over his shoulder, trying to guess what he was looking for. Maybe he was going to let her facet a stone herself. Ever since she'd started seeking him out in this little wooden building that smelled like rocks and machine oil, he'd been talking her through the process, telling her as he worked how he started with the crown, then cut the girdle, finished on the long pavilion facets. He'd told her dozens of times about the angles involved. Mae looked at the glowing stones on the tray she held. The thought that she might create something so beautiful stopped her breath.

But when her grandfather emerged from the cupboard, he didn't have the equipment for pre-shaping facet rough. Instead he held a clunky and strange-looking microscope with two eyepieces jutting from its head and an electrical cord running from its blocky base. This he plugged into the same outlet that fed his lap. After setting the microscope up on his workbench and fiddling with its knobs and levers, he turned back to Mae. She thought he was going to explain now, but all he offered was a wink as he plucked a light blue sapphire from her tray. He placed the stone on the platform above the base and pushed a button. A light came on, leaking from louvers in the base's walls and shining upward through the gem. He bent to peer through the eyepieces, made final tweaks to the settings. Then he pulled a chair over that she could stand on to see into the microscope. "The universe awaits," he said.

Half-certain this must be some kind of trick, some sleight of hand he'd rigged for her benefit, she climbed onto the chair and fitted her eyes to the viewers. It took a second to adjust to her new magnified vision. Below, she encountered an ice-colored field filled with indeterminate streaks and specks and, right in its center, something iridescent that looked like a strange lily-pad. She knew this was no trick. The lily-pad's core was dark, but it was surrounded by a delicate leaf with edges of pure, sharp light.

"What is it?" she whispered.

Her grandfather chuckled, whispered back, "That's a halo fracture around a zircon crystal. See how the break catches all those colors?"

They spent the next several hours putting one sapphire after another under the microscope, magnifying the bits of matter frozen inside. Her grandfather was right: it was like looking into the far reaches of outer space. These were regions populated by striking formations and curious nebulae. She saw rounded garnet grains hanging in clusters. She saw six-sided flecks of colorless mica and six-sided slabs of black hematite. She saw shimmering curtains of rutile silk that made her think of halls of mirrors. And all of it suspended in the hearts of stones she had previously thought were perfectly clear.

It was in a yellow sapphire that she first came upon the variety of inclusion that would become her favorite. Her grandfather had just switched out the stone under the microscope, and he took some time refocusing the apparatus on the new one. When at last it was ready for her, she put her face to the viewers. By now she was used to the random spots and flecks. Her eyes went straight to the elliptical disk of bubbles floating just off center in the sun-colored expanse. The bubbles were fine and clear and densely packed, arranged in tight curves and whorls.

"They call that a fingerprint inclusion," her grandfather told her.

Once he said it, it was unmistakable. The thing was a fingerprint—not one belonging to a human, clearly, but a fingerprint just the same—preserved like an insect in amber inside one of her grandfather's fossil stars. Its very existence seemed a miracle.

He smiled when she said this aloud.

"It's no miracle, sweetheart," he said. "They aren't even rare. You see them all the time in corundum."

And yet, she never tired of them. From that point on, every chance she had, she spent over the microscope, looking for those intricate clouds of bubbles. Like real fingerprints, their variety was endless. In some, the bubbles were almost uniform pinpricks. In others, the bubbles stretched into long, thin tubes. Some prints occurred in isolation. Others were crowded by guest crystals. They came in ovals, in irregular shapes with rounded edges, in long smears and smudges, in veils that condensed in one place and broke apart in another. No matter how they manifested themselves,

Mae had for a long time found their presence reassuring; she saw in them the personal mark of God, or maybe of the universe itself—the mark, anyway, of some vast and nearly eternal thing that she could only vaguely conceptualize. But following Bentley's conviction, the idea of fingerprints in sapphires had started to seem to her like a cruel joke, a bit of dead-end evidence, the mark of a canny criminal who had no record. Sure, they had the print, could photograph it and put it on file. They knew someone was responsible. But there was no way to trace that print to its owner.

This was what Mae was thinking about as she stood behind the counter in her shop watching the clock over the door count down to closing: fingerprints and fault. About how all the choices she had made and not made over the course of her life had winnowed down to this one exact place and time. About how, at this moment, there was no other place she could be, no other self she could inhabit.

She tapped a pen on the counter. Thirty minutes to go and the family of four still hadn't returned. She changed the roll of paper in the credit card machine and waited. When the family still hadn't come back after another ten minutes, she grabbed her keys and went to retrieve them.

* * *

When Mae parked at the mine, the mother and one of the boys were already at their car, the boy sitting sideways on the backseat with his legs out the open door while the mother inspected one of his shins. A first-aid kit sat by her side. As Mae approached, she saw the boy's leg was raw most of the distance between his knee and ankle. Though he was no longer crying, his eyes were red, his breath coming in chokes and gasps. A glob of snot hung under his nose.

"Is he all right?" Mae asked.

"It's just a scrape." The mother daubed some kind of ointment on the leg. "He slipped playing king of the mountain."

Now that she was closer, Mae saw the wound was a shallow abrasion, not as severe as it first looked.

The mother pulled a gauze pad from the first-aid kit and applied it.

"It was time to call it a day anyway," Mae said to no one in particular. Then, to the mother, "Where are the others?"

Without looking up the mother said, "Still down there, digging."

Mae left the mother and the boy to their bandages and walked to the top of the ramp that led into the mine. In the background Hauser Lake shone like a mirror, reflecting an upside-down image of the Big Belts folding back on one another. Slanting sunlight cast the entire scene in soft, warm colors. It was a postcard landscape, the kind she sometimes held in her memory until it became hard and crystalline, a cut and polished reminder of the majestic things in this world. Of course, included in that diamond memory would be flaws—herself, the father and boy in the pit, the mother and boy in the car—impurities that were small but ugly, impossible to ignore.

Something like an ache settled over her bones. Below, in the cool shadows of the mine, the father stooped over a rocker box, sifting gravel with manic furor. From this distance he appeared to have remained clean, free of sweat and dust and the grime of digging, entirely out of place. He was shouting, "Bring me some more of the good stuff, Joey!"

The boy he addressed was nowhere in sight, probably still running willy-nilly through the mine.

Mae gathered herself and started down the ramp, ready to be done with these dilettante treasure hunters. She should have chased them off at the start. It wasn't until she reached the midpoint of the descent that she finally spotted the boy lying on his belly against the gravel deposit, so coated with dirt he could have passed for a natural feature. With one hand he was scraping at the lowest layer of sediment, his arm sunk past his elbow into the earth. He'd obviously been at it for some time. Mae felt a sudden and overwhelming urge to slap both the mother and the father. How could they allow one of their children to undercut the wall? Hadn't she told them to dig from the top?

She drew her breath, started to yell at the boy to get away from there, but her warning never reached him. While her voice was still caught between her teeth and tongue, a section of the wall above the boy's prone figure gave way, dissolving into gravel and loose dirt. It wasn't a dramatic collapse. There was no giant plume of dust. No thunderous clap. Really almost no noise or dust at all from where Mae stood, only a soft whump, as though someone had dropped a sandbag on the ground. And just like that, the boy was buried. It happened so fast it was as if she had imagined it. As if that pile of rubble had always been there and she'd only mistaken it for the shape of a boy digging.

Everything froze. Mae stood on the ramp, dumb, her joints wooden and stiff. The father leaned on the rocker box, head turned toward the source of the noise, a blank expression on his face. All of creation seemed muted. The moment stretched and stretched, pulling tight against itself. Finally, just as it was getting unbearable, something snapped, and a jerky, unnatural motion returned to the world. Even as Mae started running, a part of her remained distant, almost dispassionate. It was like she was watching herself in a silent film. She saw herself stumble, slip once as she reached the mine floor, slip again in the crossing, taking a fall that would probably turn her hip sore and blue. The observing Mae felt nothing. She watched as she pushed herself up, shouted something to the father, then resumed her ungainly, unpracticed run. While this was taking place, she tried to calculate how much earth had fallen on the boy. Certainly the weight of it would have forced the oxygen from his lungs, but it probably wasn't enough to crush him outright. Which meant it wasn't too late. The boy still had time, if they were quick.

The father reached the pile of earth first and attacked it with his shovel. Mae got there a few seconds later, diving onto her knees to plunge her hands into the dirt. It was the sensation of rocks scraping the flesh from her knuckles and breaking her nails that finally brought her back to herself. The film ended, and all the panic and adrenaline and noise flooded back in. "God, no," the father was saying, over and over in time with his shovel strokes.

Mae scrabbled and scratched, willing herself to push her hands through all the worthless stones and dirt and fossil stars. There was still time for this boy. If only she could find and grasp his wrist, his finger, they would be able to get him out. It wasn't too late. This was a boy she could save.

The Nimrod Literary Awards
The Pablo Neruda Prize for Poetry

Honorable Mention
Grant Gerald Miller

My Father Knocked a Hole in the Sky

with a wooden hammer. He refused to speak of night. Preferred the chiseled horizons of morning. Liked things to be underwater where he could look down at their murky forms and guess what shape they would take when he fished them out with his stone hands.

When the sun rose slick and pink like an infant, my father set out to follow the sweeping light. He traced blue streets under clouds that refused to stay still in search of an earlier part of day. He hammered at the air like he was incapable of hurting it. After he broke

the sky, my father set to the woods. At dusk he sat on the porch and dabbed at the sweat that pooled on his skin. He looked over the forest where he'd left nothing but stumps and waited for dusk, and those tricks of light that make things appear to grow.

Skin

I still really haven't told you about my mother. I remember her eyes before they were replaced with skin. They were brown and speckled like quail eggs.

They looked at me like I held something together, like I'd hung these planets in space and set them in motion. I shot our dog with a BB gun as he sniffed the fence. I blasted tiny holes in milk jugs filled with water. I sold the gun for ten dollars at a yard sale.

Before the man bought it he said, "Es esto real?" I wanted to show him the milk jugs, the pock-marked fence, the dog that refused to trust me. My mother stood inside, looking out the window, closing her eyes and opening them, unsure of what she was watching.

What Is Left to Say of Birds

cutting through the air, searching for dregs on the scattered ground. Even the moon is wordless and wingless.

All we want is flight, ever since we were children on our soiled mattresses, wishing away the other side of the door.

At night you raise your arm in your sleep, point to the sky as if you are about to say something, to grab something that is just out of reach. I guide your arm toward me. Sleep is a luxury that flutters at the wrong

times. We are birds soaring wordless in the night, worrying over the strength of our nests, dreaming of flying to the next thing on the ground that will sustain us for as long as it will.

THE NIMROD LITERARY AWARDS
The Pablo Neruda Prize for Poetry

FINALIST
EMILY ROSE COLE

The Contortionist

Tonight, I visit the bigtop alone,
the black air thick with lightning

and fryer oil. I take center ring,
lie flat under the trapeze rig
and pinwheel an elbow

beneath a leg, tip my chin to kiss
the sag of the net, and look
for the boy
who jumped last year,
a freak

accident, they said. Except

I saw whipped tiger's eyes
in his eyes, saw him cupping
the strongman's cock
like he meant it.

He told me once that he only felt alive
in the air, spare body hung
between bar and bar.

I called him Anya,

like he asked, but I didn't think of him

as *she* until she was sprawled
on the loose dirt, arm pinned
beneath a knee like the spent
arch of a ballerina's foot.

But when they switched
his eyelids shut and said *he's gone,*
I didn't dare correct them.

Now, she trembles
at the platform's edge
like a shadow. Under the net,
I pleat my feet like palms in prayer

and I wonder if she can still smell

popcorn and wet elephant shit,
if she still loves the calliope
and the way a tongue collapses
cotton candy, its fragile net
of melting sugar.

Anya lifts her heels,
poised to leap.

I see her
suspended, blurred

fingers opening

for a bar

that will not

swing

Poem in Which You Are Joan of Arc's Lover

You expect it to begin like a battle,
but there's no bite in her. She doesn't kiss
you, doesn't coo like the girl she is.

You jut your hips like you own her.
It's strange to you that her tunic smells
of myrrh and smoke and saltpeter.

When you try to frame her face
in your fingers, she pins you
with her eyes until you do as you're told:

plus dur, plus fort, plus, plus, plus.
You almost expect her to cry
out, but when she unhooks

her mouth and flashes her eyes,
blank and white as salt, she does not name
saints or gods, but fortresses—

Saint Loup, Jean-le-Blanc—and tactics
gasped in a strange language: *Advance
advance. Hold the line. Steady now. Steady.*

She makes you feel as if you're all
the army she needs, until her vision
clears and she's not a vessel anymore,

just a girl waving you to the door,
scrambling to scrawl heaven's help
on the map tucked under her pillow.

You know now that if you sink
your hands into her hair,
God will tongue lightning

down your back, that only a girl
like her could bathe all of France
in the holy milk of her eyes.

Asked if I Miss My Mother, I Say I Miss the House

Even if I never see it again, that house holds me:
I wander everywhere, dropping a trail
of fingernails curved like swan necks—

Seven years and twelve addresses later, the lace
of mud I tracked on that carpet still looks like veins
in a bee's wing. The hardwood still hums

with hymns she sang odd hours, the plucked
strings of the harp I built but did not build
alone. The walls still ring with the warnings

of train whistles, the jar on my nightstand
still full of mashed pennies with their faces
rubbed off. Once, she strung them into wind

chimes, hung them over the porch. They didn't hold.
Ice shook them down, a hail of warped copper
crushing the snowdrops. That house is a dream

waiting for my head to nod, a labyrinth
doubling back on itself, tree rings missing
a center. I will follow the trail I made

until I stumble across the door—
I will nibble it down each day
as if it were made of bread.

SEMI-FINALIST

ROCHELLE GOLDSTEIN

Gretel's Answer

In this darkness they call a forest
the animals stare with their
jeweled eyes—

Who keeps watch over a life?

The birds will eat the crumbs and,
without knowing where we've been,
how can we find our way?

Soon we will no longer see—
we will have to remember
every step we are about to take.

Resurrection is the fairytale.

Why have you made me lose my way—
you who were supposed to look out for me?

Let me have the faith to walk through
this unchartered place into meaning.
Home is not a place at all:
we have eaten it, and it has eaten us.

There was a time when my feet were
planted very close to the rose bushes—

even with their thorns, with the bees
who hovered looking for sweetness,
I was happy.

But I was trained along the trellis,
kept out of the way, and so learned to follow.

In my next life, I wish to be wild,
at home anywhere,
growing inside a creviced hand.

I will make a suitcase of my heart

and everything I need will be neatly folded,
so I could leave at a moment's notice.

Christopher Woods, *Creek and Trees,* photograph

THE NIMROD LITERARY AWARDS

The Pablo Neruda Prize for Poetry

FINALIST

KATHARYN HOWD MACHAN

Paws

Keep talking. How did the story go?
—Sara Eliza Johnson in "Marchen"

It's always the wolf. Count on it.
Hunger just outside the door
and the distant church bell ringing.
Little girl in a crimson cap,
small boy sneaking out through the gate,
young pigs behind flimsy walls.
Even the brother and sister abandoned
would have been swallowed by shining eyes
if the witch hadn't taken them in.

The oldest stories are the oldest stories
until they turn true again,
each one a shard of mirror
piercing our softest flesh.
Monks may sing in midnight choir,
but how far does their music reach?
Look to the basket, the swallowed duck,
the straw and the sticks shuttered tight.
The wolf grins. Bet your life.

I haven't lived more than sixty years
without learning a tale or three.
Where do my poems come from?
Told to lie still, shut up, keep secrets,
dark weight like a rat on my brain,
and me just one of the many many
praying the wolf will be caught and cut
or shot or burned or boiled to death
so he'll never howl again.

My Beast

walks to the cupboard, reaches in,
drinks too much red wine and vomits
words about a treacherous mother
who smoked cigarettes, wore thin high heels,
stayed up nights sipping hardcore whiskey

from a lipstick-crimsoned glass.
Walks miles and thinks the world is flat
as music from a broken piano
abandoned when the composer died
alone in a small blue room.

Dresses in a ragged cape aflame
with shivering orange-yellow candles
that give no heat nor light but never
cease their tiny birthday burning.
Rapes my daughter with a smile

on his face, teeth pumpkin-rotting black.
Hands my granddaughter a smooth
scarlet cap, a perfect white rose,
a key he tells her she must never use
to open the door to his wild crooked heart.

On Loving

If you learn a lesson well enough
you don't do the impish thing again.
Instead you begin backing up
the harddrive, keep a keen eye
for rusty roofing nails on the sidewalk,
skip the last round of tequila.
You'd think by now I'd say no more.
And yes.

Weeks ago I stood at a crosswalk
and couldn't tell if the breeze
came from the wind or the cars plowing by.
I barter often with the sky
that hangs over Friendly Avenue,
will it to caution me
with dusk too quick on an afternoon run,
a sudden summer storm.

Some choices don't want to be made.
Like you on the phone about to get
your discount spaceship tattoo.
If you don't like it, then maybe
this isn't meant to be.
As if you have no demands of me,

but you'd peel the kisses off my lips
from other men if you could.
How unreasonable and how like love:
that black cloud rearing unexpectedly
to spite the persistent sun, their squabble
unavoidable, celestial, and so routinely lit.

Sadly, Everything's in Flux

Say the body falls
for the unerring
music of a baritone sax

at three in the morning
wafting from the one house
with lights on. Heraclitus

could be down on his luck
& stopped,
despite the rain & him

without an umbrella,
by the vagrant
strands of that sax—

someone's breath, stinking
of sorrow,
pushed through a reed

& transformed into music
that can halt a sage
in the midst of

inclement weather. The worst
to be said is
the body's not enough

to long for. Say it is
the past, always,
that calls us out

of ourselves, that gives
rise to the flesh
imagining it's more, & nothing,

let it be said, can come
of any of this
but loss & its lover,

grief. Longing *has legs,*
as they say, & is
in this for the duration.

Let Heraclitus be invited in
by a woman
with a hot cup of coffee,

the light behind her
weaving her shadow
& the dim trembling

cast by the coffee's steam
into some myth.
Or let him be

drinking Tullamore Dew
in some corner bar,
remembering a woman

who's more than a myth.
Let the alcohol
preserve some stray memory,

all anyone would need
to remember. *Nothing*
needs changing, let Heraclitus

whisper into the ear of a woman
asleep after love,
rain—the lazy signature

of whatever gods monitor,
still, men & women—
no more than a drizzle,

a kind of hesitant longing
for a body held
so long ago it's almost gone.

Christopher Woods, photograph

The Nimrod Literary Awards

The Pablo Neruda Prize for Poetry

Honorable Mention

Emily Van Kley

Until the Heavens Ring

I'm a preacher's daughter—
split me open & I'll spill words
dressed up in stoles & black

glasses, clauses fervent
as matchbooks & solemn
as brass-snuffed candles,

each line striving to beat a path
from the made to the maker—
what luck if the difference turns

out to be semantic—oh yes &
the stretched drum of my
heart always trying to lift up

its voice & sing. What I mean
to imply is intellect. Or sex.
But only allegorically.

We are a people who try not
to lead by example. If we
are to arrive at the body

we prefer first to circle back
through a great deal of cloud.
In grade five basement rooms

clamorous with the tooth
clacking of electric typewriters,
it was correct to leave two

spaces after each period.
Now, sentences sit
closer. No need to draw

out the distance between end &
beginning. Only the thumb
still sometimes hovers

over the space bar, wondering
if something more ought
to be done. O, the Word

made Flesh! We've had
a lifetime of trouble with both
already. Fortunately we know

to rejoice in our sufferings,
for suffering produces
perseverance, & perseverance

character, & character
a certain feeling in the chest
which might be guilt

& might be gratitude, & which
suggests by its very presence
the possibility of some One

in a position to receive.

Superior

Lamprey ribbons
sturgeon's steely side,

the eel's nightmare mouth
circular, bladed, a roulette wheel

of teeth. Its first cut
sharp & painless, cautious

as a surgeon. No blood
wasted. The great fish

hulks on. Its dinosaur
snout & toothless bite

falsely rumored to claim
the toes & nose-tips of children

who paddle too far out
in limb-slowing water,

their lips purpled, the cold
antiseptic—what doesn't kill you

will make you stronger,
their parents like to say.

But lamprey knows better:
that strength may be siphoned.

The great fish pales.
The lake vasts & voids.

* * *

My parents reached Superior
in November of '75. The Edmund

Fitzgerald newly wrecked
near the Canadian border.

The wind magnificent,
waves not yet smoothed

over for the approach of a ballad.
Their Dodge Dart anchored

to road by casserole dishes,
quilted flannel, Jerry Jeff Walker

records, everything worth saving
from the Sioux Center trailer they abandoned

to ghost its winter plain.
When you are practiced

at the hollowed-egg art of leaving
only the inviolate & disdainful

can make an impression.
My parents decided to stay.

Already then, lamprey razored
the currents of the St. Lawrence.

Sturgeon's reign was going
the way of Goliath. Paper &

steel. Ore ships looming
low as loons, occasionally snapping

their steel bones on the water's
intemperance. My parents became

as those who lived at water's edge,
who dressed in sheepskin mittens

& boiled wool mufflers,
shoveled snow regardless of heart

conditions, & didn't make
a fuss out of waiting for spring.

Shoshana Kertesz, photograph

Varsity Athletics

I'd leave the high school gym,
hips bruised from what Coach

called digging. Too short to play
the front row, I'd watch

the tall girls, how they lined
up like fenceposts

at the net, how they leapt
and hammered the ball

past the other team's faces.
The trick was to hit limp-wristed,

so your hand snapped down.
Like a faggot, Coach would say.

I'd step outside and the cold
would be broken glass.

The streetlights would be ice-
tasseled. My damp hair

would freeze like a wild
chandelier around the winter-dim

lamp of my expression. When a gust
came through, snow would stop

as if flashbulbed, and I would
stop too, my hot muscles

locked, a hitch in the small
weather system of my breath.

The moment would suspend
longer than was strictly

necessary. I'd stay past the point
of thighs gone raw with cold

under sateen trackpants,
past snow released to gallop

off in another direction,
past thoughts of my mother's

eight sisters—women enough
to field a high school volleyball team

(too bad they never showed much
interest in athletics), past

the storm canceling specificity,
mounding street signs, parked

cars, liquor bottles
tossed along the sidewalk,

blanketing my little blooming
heart of a faggot. Exactly,

not exactly. I'd thank
winter for its status

as neither friend nor foe,
receive the satisfaction

of no answer. Only then budge
my ice-block toes—they'd be white

by the time I reached home,
I'd have to rub them back

to usefulness—and start
as if from nowhere, my tracks

behind covered over, senses
scoured in lake-effect wind.

THE NIMROD LITERARY AWARDS
The Pablo Neruda Prize for Poetry

FINALIST
JEANNE WAGNER

The Night You Come out to Your Parents

for Brian

the scent of Clorox makes you think
  immaculate
just as the stiff napkins   standing plate-side
make you conscious of the white
  bone china
how it's an appetite waiting for color
for its complement of gristle
  and flesh
soon you'll be served asparagus spears
  those gently
absurd over-cooked phalluses
you look down at
while your father tells the Liberace joke
  again
and light sieves in from the screen door
  pixelating
the air   leaving a smudge
  that hovers
over the table like the opposite
  of grace

Madame Cezanne Sits for Her Portrait While Facing Still Life with Curtain

His colors crowd each other, cling to forms
both averted and displayed, the way I feel
before the gaze of a camera, or the eyes of
my husband who stands a little ways away.

Because he needs to hide me, he crosses
my legs, tilts my chin, presses my arms
to my side. Only with a still life will he
allow the plane of the canvas to slide

forward a little, so that apples roll in their
crowded bowls, a shapely pitcher shows
its plump-rose glaze, a white serviette
disrobes while the lemon's puckered

omphalos winks like an eye. I watch
the chameleon-flush of skin and rind,
see how the naked fruit-majas recline,
nuzzling each other like newborn mice.

But I'm all stretched plane, hair tied back,
my eyes trained on this still life with its
curtain and flowered pitcher, a pall of
shadows pooling in the white porcelain.

I wonder, were the apples picked or fallen?
What of the black and green curtain with
its waist pulled tight? He used black as
a backdrop before. It must stand for night,

a camera's shroud. The absence against
which he casts me in his carnal play of
light. When anyone asks him about color,
he always tells them, *It's biological.*

Why She Wasn't Invited to Join the Geological Society of London

Mary Anning (1799–1847) was a British fossil collector, dealer, and paleontologist who became known around the world for important finds she made in Jurassic marine fossils.
—Wikipedia

At first, she hunts only with her father, finds fossils the way
a poor person finds things,

looks for the random glint of a penny in the gutter, the wink
of its coppery sheen.

At daybreak, she goes out with him wanting to see a day
spilling its light on sand,

but finds the sea's wildness instead, finds the wind making
a bonnet of her hair;

finds a basket on her arm, full of what the Blue Lias holds
out for her.

And because she sells what she finds as trinkets to tourists,
peddles them

in the open, the way a woman might sell her own beauty
to a willing buyer,

or the way a gypsy might hawk her charms, calling them
snake-stones, devil's fingers,

calling them common names; a common woman, half-
educated, unmarried,

with coarse hands, wind-licked hag-hair, hems savaged
by sea salt.

Because sometimes when she delivers a skeleton from
its womb of limestone and shale,

she feels more of a midwife than a scholar; she thinks
of her favorites,

the ammonites, spherical, fetal, curving into themselves
like stillborn things.

Because, like the Devil, she unleashes monsters: chimeras,
griffins and basilisks,

bodies unbiblical, unsanctified, otherworldly, unholy.
Puts them in her parlor,

the ungainly necks, the beaks, the long enviable wing
bones reaching out for flight.

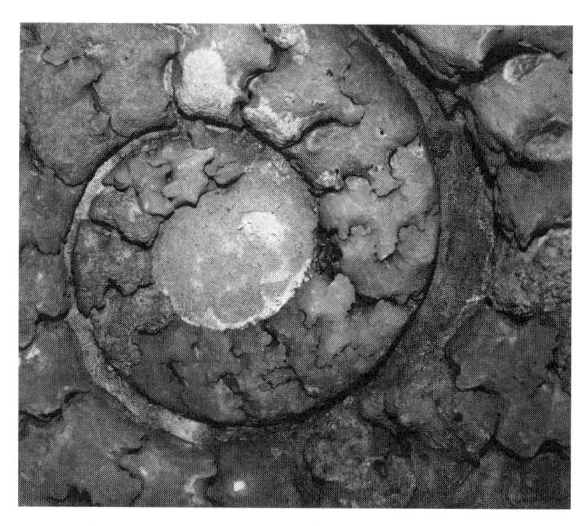

Eleanor Leonne Bennett, photograph

Second Prize
Emily Wortman-Wunder

Burning

We woke that night to the dogs barking like it was the end of the world, and, to hear the mushheads at the office tell it, it was. The boys sent away, Henry transferred to Idaho, me back in my own apartment, alone again. But it's been an eon and a half since I paid them any mind. I'm up on the mesa with the best of them, old firefighter Ray, and though last fall's entire disaster is spread out below me—the angry swath where the Dago Bird Refuge used to be, the Forest Service compound with its tiny American flag, the three burnt hulks of the snowplows Henry and I are still paying for—I'm cool with it. I can feel the coolness within me like a potable spring.

Then the radio in my breast pocket gives a staticky, "Ten-four, Nancy, let's get her started," and I turn around and blast the underside of the nearest oakbrush with a ribbon of flame. At first it just shrivels the leaves and blackens the bark, but pretty soon a crack of molten orange opens up. I wait until I've made sure it's going to catch and then I walk down the road, counting my paces, fifty yards until the next blast of flame. I look back up at my first one and it's smudging nicely, not too hot but a good slow smolder that should take all morning to work its way uphill. It's the middle of March and a perfect day for burning, overcast and still. God, it's good to get out of the office. I take a deep breath and swing back my hair.

I blast and scan, tracing where the fire will eat through the choking green, from the road up to the chalk cliffs where Ray and I have cut our fireline. All oakbrush. Once we've burned this slope over the deer will come back, the hawks will hunt here again, and I'm thinking maybe, if we're lucky, we'll get Lewis's woodpeckers. At the office we emphasize the practical aspect of prescribed burns. Less fuel, less chance of catastrophic fire, Ray will say, laying his hands palm down on the Formica conference table. Only once the district ranger's nodding will I add the bit about the wildlife. "These systems need fire," I finish, "to clean them out." I do not say, *to let them breathe*: too spiritual for this crowd.

Plus it's just a hair too close. They'd get it. They'd make the leap. Brush, family, overgrowth, fire. Renewal. And the pity would be back, unbearable, unbalancing. How can I put this so they believe me? Four years ago, it was me, my dog Bette, and my truck; now it's me, Bette, my truck, and a decent apartment. In the middle there was—what? One mess after another.

Ray's firing his way up toward where I am. He's got his ponytail tucked into the collar of his shirt and even from here I can tell he is frowning with concentration, looking each oakbrush up and down for the best spot to aim his torch. Ray's a good guy. He's the only one at the office that hasn't come at me with his false concern, his voice hushed with the Gravity of it all, hasn't tried to corner me behind some closed door so I can Tell Him What I Really Feel. Maybe that's because Ray, with his wife, Rita, was our friend from before; maybe it's just his way: gentle and discreet (the polar opposite of me). I don't know and I don't ask.

He moves slower than I do, scientific and cautious, still getting used to this idea of fire as good. We've been the prescribed burn team for two years and he's more serious about it now than I am, I think. He's always photocopying articles from the *Fire Management Journal* and leaving them on my desk. But under the precision and the pondering he's got a firefighter's heart, big and red and tender to the slightest curl of smoke. Destruction makes him nervous.

I, on the other hand, love fire, the way it's almost alive, the way it transforms everything. Take anything from around me now and notice how it feeds my excitement. The stench of the propane, the weight of the torch at the end of my arm, its blackened nozzle, even my cracked and burnished work gloves. I send a blast of flame shooting up over my head, burning a juniper from the top down, just the way they tell you not to. I squat to light a huge dry branch lying in the road, then heave it up into the brush, a little advance sortie. The motion almost blows it out, and I hold my breath until I see the flame creep back, curling over the top of the stick and spilling out into the dry leaves around it.

Henry used to accuse me of preferring fire to people, specifically such people as him and the boys. He used to say if I had my way I'd live in an efficiency apartment with one of every bare necessity, one knife, one fork, one pair of underwear, all neatly lined up in the closet. I told him if I had one pair of underwear I'd be wearing it. But secretly we both knew he was right, and I even thought about those spats as I signed the lease this winter, and had to smile. Whatever else, Henry certainly knew me. Without him and the boys, my life is clean and simple. I get home, roam the hills with Bette until dark, and then we both have our kibble and bits and straighten ourselves for the following day. My boots have never been so well polished, my gear never in better repair, and I even have time to brush Bette's teeth with an old toothbrush and a little baking soda, the way she likes.

* * *

As I burn, my mind can drift back. There's no territory too dangerous when I've got a propane torch in my hand, you could say, or maybe it's the weather, moody and quiet, and no one crowding in on me. I'm like Janis Joplin, gargantuan beside Henry, who looked like he just finished riding the Preakness. The boys were both rodeo heartthrobs, cherubic blonds with brown eyes. We once made the mistake of having a family studio portrait done and we could never bring ourselves to hang it up, it's that unnerving. I called it the Manson Family Rides Again. Henry took it down to his desk and managed to lose it within a month. And the photo didn't even hint at the squabbles we had. Face it, I find myself telling an imaginary audience, some families are better off apart.

Evan, fourteen, and Chris, ten. Early on I asked Henry about their mother. "Up and left one day," he said. "Wanted nothing to do with them or me." That was all. His disgust told me everything I needed to know, I thought, and I took it as a warning. I couldn't even tell you now what I thought I'd been warned against. But I kept my distance, mostly. My job was to make jokes, keep things light. I let Henry be the parent and I was more like the laughing godmother. The godmother who slept with their dad, of course.

Take that time Evan spray-painted naked women on the back of the Forest Service office building. Almost a year ago. It's not a capital crime, is what I said. And they were interesting naked women, some skinny, some fat, some wearing Coco Chanel hats and carrying pocketbooks. They're kinda cute, I told Henry. He refused to laugh. I told him the office needed new paint anyway, and he said I was missing the point. "Oh, Hanky, what is the point?" I groaned, and he said, "The point is, you've got to take things seriously some of the time. This is bigger than a stupid wall. This is his life. This is *our* life. Sometimes I may not want to take it seriously either but I have to—that's my job. Get it?" And there was a moment there that we stared each other down, for a long minute seeing each other the way everyone else sees us, until I caught the twitch under his mustache and reached out to tweak his skinny little belly. Chris came in then, sidling up between us the way he always did when our fights were over, and I assumed that was the end of it.

* * *

This is what I love about the field: there's nothing right now but the sound of boots on gravel and the hiss of my propane tank. I continue down the hill, the walking a sort of meditation. My mind wanders, my eyes wander. I can't see the CDOT burn or the Forest Service compound anymore, so instead I look wide, twenty miles across the river to the opaque shadows of Nipple Peak and beyond. It's raining over there, or snowing, even. Good. A heavy, windless rain is what we need this afternoon.

So far, so good. All Ray and I have talked about today is logistics. When I come to the end of my line I sit on the truck bumper and watch him, the way he lifts up the edges of the underbrush delicately, really thinking before he points his flame. He sets his feet down the same way, avoiding ruts and rocks. Slow, steady, focused but oblivious. Is this fondness I'm feeling? I ask myself for amusement's sake, but I have to think about it. Is that what this odd lightness across my shoulders is called? Or is it merely relief at being out of the office? For all that I can tell a good story I'm the village idiot when it comes to feelings, and I guess that's one of the things I always liked about Henry: he knew his. Anger, horniness, corniness, love. And he knew I had mine under the crazy stories and the smartass jokes. I got used to him reading me before I did, and it throws me, now, to have to come up with the terminology on my own. Not that anyone's seriously trying, that presumptuous prying at the office aside. I shift one of my boots on the gravel, its weight dragging the rest of my leg along.

Ray comes up to me, saying, "She's looking good. Firing well. And this cloudcover ought to keep her in check."

I agree. This is the sort of material my conversations are made of these days. The conversations I allow, at least. No more agonizing over whether to ground Evan *again* or try to figure out something more creative. No more arguing about whether study hall is a class and whether it's morally if not legally okay to skip it. No more pointless wondering if Henry and I can have something together that isn't about the boys.

Ray and I stand twenty feet apart or so, facing up the oak-brush slope that is starting to catch and smolder, the smoke drifting down and settling into our clothes and hair. I'm about to say something smartass when Ray speaks instead.

"We're getting some elk burgers and the last of the apricot preserves out this weekend. Clean out the pantry and the freezer before the summer gets going. Rita said to ask you. Our treat."

My heart sinks and I wish I didn't have to answer. "I was sort of thinking of heading over to Denver this weekend," I lie. "Visit my sister, shop some."

Ray pokes his head forward with approval. "Keep up with the family, yes," he says. "The two of you are close, I remember. Got to hold onto that."

We're not close, my sister and I. We bore each other.

"Yeah, family. What a joy," I mutter, throwing my gear into the back of the truck. It's time to start for the top of the burn, to make sure we keep the damage under control. I hear Ray clear his throat behind me and I start the truck, rev the gas over anything he might be saying.

He waits until we're driving to continue. "How're things going, then?"

This is not, not, not a conversation I want to have, at this particular moment. At any particular moment. "Oh, fine," I answer. "Really, fine."

I drive fast, up past where we've been torching all morning, gunning into the soft mud in the shadow of the roadcut, slipping a little, pulling free. I tell myself he needed to say his little piece, to get it out, and now he'll let it go. I hope this, anyhow, but suspect he's still chewing on something over there because he keeps making these fake coughs and fluffing himself.

Coming up is the part of the road we talk about in safety meetings, where it narrows to the width of a pickup and erosion has eaten it away on the drop-off side. If he were to look out his window now, Ray could see two hundred feet down to the remains of the last truck that took this curve too fast. Ray's got his eyes straight ahead. We're supposed to take this section at a crawl but I don't brake. I steer into the bank, not so much that we bounce off it but enough to lift the tires on the driver's side and tilt us more sharply toward the cliffs. I see a rut edge that will keep us level if I catch it just right. I don't so much steer as finesse the wheel, smoothing my hand across it like I'm flattening a bedsheet. At twenty-five miles an hour it's an impressive move, one only a few folks at the Forest Service could pull off. Only a few people would even try, and believe me, Ray may be a firefighter but he isn't one of them. I make it. I glance over at him without moving my head. I'm hoping I've shut him up, but I can't tell.

At the crest of the next switchback I turn in at the fireline we've cut. Hacked-off oakbrush branches squeal against the paint and it's loud enough in the cab that we don't have to talk anymore. I drive to the end, where the slope is in permanent shadow and still harbors snow. There's a smell here like winter, which makes me think, for no reason, of the herons. We get out and start uncoiling the hoses.

Ray goes out one way with one hose, and I go out the other, and when we've reached as far as we can in either direction we get back in the truck and drive back toward the road. It's kind of communal and quiet, just the popping of the fire as it moves our way and the hiss of water hitting leaves. We talk, but it's basic stuff: whether the wind's changing, how the sky looks, whether the rain will come like we're hoping it will.

* * *

The night herons came back this spring. I saw the first one two weeks ago, a male, poking around the charred remains of the old heronry. I squatted in the weeds for an hour watching him through my binoculars; he'd poke through the unburnt stuff, finicky, and wade along the shore where the tamarisk still shaded it. He'd fly off for a while, and then come back, and forage some more. Right at dusk he lifted his head and took off, flying in the direction of the river. They'll nest somewhere else until the preserve grows back, I guess.

"They look like puppets!" Chris said the first time I brought him out to the preserve for some birdwatching—and they do; I'd never thought of it before, but they look exactly like puppets you could pull over your forearm, just that shape and awkward and careful, the way puppets would move. The birdwatching was pretty much against my rules but we both liked it enough that I made an exception. Two or three times a month we'd pack sandwiches and head out at first light, just the two of us, never talking much except to point out birds.

The month before the fire Chris and I had snuck up to the night heron nest and watched the chicks, two strapping healthy things with the ugliest awkwardest fuzz you could imagine. It felt a little like we were playing hooky, leaving Henry and Evan alone to sleep off their latest fight. Chris leaned in, enormous-eyed, holding his breath, plucking at my elbow. "We shouldn't touch them," he decided, and instead we stroked the reeds around the nest, dipped our fingers in the icy marshwater, gently poked the dry sticks. The chicks would clack their oversize beaks at our fingers if they strayed too close, but in between their beaks would open piteously, flashing the pattern of gape and throat. Chris pulled me away so that the adult birds could return and we watched from behind an olive thicket until our knees got cold and stiff. I pulled our sandwiches out of my pack and pulled off pieces for Chris so he could watch through the binoculars and then he did the same for me, biting off a piece and giving a piece.

I tell myself that if Ray and I end up talking about the whole Henry mess today I am going to keep Chris out of it.

* * *

More than halfway down the fireline the drizzle begins and it's clear we won't need this extra strip of watered ground. Ray and I keep going anyway, without even having to consult each other. With him it's probably cautiousness and with me it's putting off the miserable wait in the truck as long as possible. We're committed to a long day here, until the fire's reached the fireline and been subdued, or peters out of its own accord.

I zip up my rain slicker and train the hose into the oakbrush below me. I watch the silvery spray battle the smoke-gray drizzle, the oakbrush drinking it all up greedily. This line of brush is spared the fire, for now, and I imagine it already sending runnels underground to take the space opened up by the burn. I know very well that oakbrush doesn't grow by runnels, but it spreads almost as fast and as thick as if it did. Part of me hates this part of the prescribed burns, where we have to put it out.

I'm remembering the last time we went camping with Ray and Rita, the last time we did anything as a family at all—almost a year ago now, last Memorial Day. We thought we were at some kind of truce, sitting around the fire with the other adults, talking about the summer to come, the fires that were already starting, down near Grand Junction, the seasonal crews we had coming on the following week, the way the whole summer was shaping up quick into a hectic replica of all the previous summers. The mosquitoes weren't out yet and the air was frigid as soon as the sun dropped into the trees: the adults were bundled into lawn chairs and the kids were playing some elaborate running game in untied sneakers and shorts. When the sun started streaking orange through the trees we called them in for bratwursts and potato salad, and Rita made everyone in her family wash their hands before eating, even Ray, who looked at us sheepishly.

"She's got him whupped," Henry said to me later, in the tent, both of us stretched out on top of the sleeping bags as long as we could stand the cold, wearing undershirts and underwear.

"'Whupped'? What the hell is that?"

"You know. 'Wash with soap, Ray, there's still dirt in the cracks of your palms.'"

"Just because she doesn't want him to get hepatitis or something he's whupped. I suppose because I make you use Kleenex instead of your shirt you're whupped too." I wouldn't have admitted it but I felt the same as Henry. We still thought what we had going was so much better than what they had, than what anyone had.

I remember how we whispered then, partly to keep our voices hidden and partly to keep an ear out for the boys' tent on the other side of the fire. When everyone was asleep we made love, quietly, getting as much in as we could before fire season came and one or the other of us was always away. Henry was happy that night, giggling and making faces until we really got into it. I put my chin on his shoulder and imagined opening myself to the stars, the two of us rutting in the cold fields like a couple of badgers. Alone and free, the offspring turned out to forage for themselves; the male meeting the female at the outer reaches of their separate territories.

A breaking branch makes me jump, but it's just the burned oakbrush settling in on itself. My fingers are starting to get clumsy from the cold and I think that if we could have always been that way—that free—maybe we would have made it. The thought makes me ache with grief and for the first time in four months I wonder what Henry's doing now. If he's out in a Targhee National Forest pickup, trying to get a feel for the new country. Or if he's stuck in a meeting somewhere, his blood pressure ticking up with every minute on the clock. No one there to pass him a goofy note or to jiggle his knee; no one there to keep things light.

* * *

By the time Ray and I finish dousing the fireline the hillside is socked in. The view has vanished, town and mountains both, so that it's just the two of us, the truck, and the smoldering hillside. The rain's running off my sleeves into my gloves and dripping off my helmet down my neck, and I'm desperately trying to dream up a task to keep me from sitting in that truck with Ray for the next few hours. He's shaking his hose, clearing it of water so it folds better and doesn't mold or freeze; he has an awkward way of doing this, leaning out over his boots and holding the heavy hose at the end of his extended arms. He looks up from it sideways. "Glad to hear you're doing well, over there," he says. Meaning my apartment, I presume, and not where I'm standing as we speak. "It's been a year of change, for sure."

"That it has."

We climb into the front seat to get out of the wet but leave the doors open, our legs slung out the sides. The silence builds up between us.

"Looks like we might have to burn again next week," Ray says. "To get all of it."

I nod.

We get out our lunches. Ray has a sandwich, probably made for him by Rita, that's bulging with fresh produce, and a dinner roll spread with homemade jam. I've got three cheese-and-cracker packs, slightly crushed. I try not to look envious, although I can already taste the way my mouth will feel after all this salt. On my good days I used to make five sandwiches of a morning, one each for myself and the boys and two for Henry. I'd never been a sandwich person—all that assembly—but I got pretty good at it. I liked standing in the kitchen in the half-dark, putting sandwiches and chips and cut-up carrots into little baggies while the guys stumbled through the shower, one after another.

All that ended after the boys moved to their mother's in Florida. The trailer was deadly silent, like a museum. I'd clean something, straighten the magazines on the table, vacuum the rug, and it would stay just as I'd set it for days. Even Bette and Bruno seemed to tiptoe around. I kept expecting to find Henry crying, or for some little thing to set him off to where we could open up into it, scream, hold each other again, but everything stayed fixed and perfect. I would pat Henry on the shoulder and it was like patting the couch. My total fantasy of married life, Henry to myself and not a single fight, and I could barely breathe.

Ray wipes a mud smear off the dash with his sleeve. "I guess I've never been clear what happened," he says, glancing at me. "That stuff with the boys?" He's nervous, which is what throws me off my guard, I'll decide later. It makes me think I can do this: he's just curious. I think I can handle curious.

I start with the phone call, middle of the night, how the dogs leapt up like they'd been shot. Barking so loud we could hardly think. I'm going to make this good, I decide as I warm into it. Give him his money's worth. I haven't had too many chances to tell this story, and it's great to hear my old voice, hear the way it can tweak and smooth until the mess sounds like just another crazy brouhaha.

"After Henry hung up the phone," I tell Ray, "I remember I yanked on my boots. Didn't even lace them. The light was on, that big fluorescent one in the kitchen, so it was super bright, but to look at us you would've thought it was pitch black. Henry, stumbling around, me, stumbling around, Henry already pissed as a hornet caught in a window. The dogs crawling around the kitchen floor with their tails between their legs.

"We got to the door and the smoke about knocked us on our *backs*. Little bits of ash floating down like snow."

Ray nods—"You could smell it all the way down in town," he said.

"—I couldn't even tell you if Henry was up ahead of me, or behind me, or what, except that I could hear him yelling"—I make my voice go into a fake growl to imitate him—"'*I'm gonna get you little shits! I'm gonna kill you both!*' And I was like, oh man, better keep *Henry* out of trouble, and I wasn't even thinking about the boys. Like I couldn't grasp it yet or something, how serious it was.

"So there we were, flailing along, coming up on the district firetrucks parked along the road, and we could even see the West Divide fire crew trucks down near the CDOT, and more trucks turning up from the highway—and then we hear this explosion, and I'm like, oh, *fuck*. And Bob Brenner gets on the megaphone, and he starts telling everyone to evacuate the area, evacuate the area." I do a pretty good imitation of Bob Brenner's self-important drawl and Ray snickers a little, despite himself.

"And Henry and I pay him absolutely no attention, of course, with Henry on the warpath and me worried that he's going to make some huge fool of himself in front of the entire five-agency fire crew, and then we come up over the ridge."

I pause a moment. I remember the ridge, and how that was the second I realized this was something different than what I thought. I came up over the ridge and saw the heronry in flames, that great forked cottonwood trunk at the center of it burning away like a campfire, and it was like my heart stopped within my chest. The first thing I thought was, the herons. Then, they couldn't possibly have done this. Not the boys. Then I decided it must have been Evan. I could see him doing it, but not Chris. But there they were.

"And that's when we saw the two of them, down by the squad car already." I crumple up my cracker paper and stuff it under the seat. "Half of what the squad car's there for is to protect them from the parents, in that kind of situation. They're not dumb. Because we were livid. Well, Henry was. As the parent. Came screaming down the entire hill in that smoke, it's lucky he didn't keel over with asphyxiation. And I was pretty pissed too by that point."

I wonder how much of this story Ray's heard, and from who. If Officer Davis or any of the West Divide fire crew has told him how I was actually the one to get to the boys first, screaming like some hysterical elephant. I try not to remember this part.

"Not one of my best moments. You know, because this was the thing—they'd taken our fire gear—*these* things. The very propane tank I used today. This very helmet."

Ray shakes his head and says, "You got to wonder what those boys were thinking. Got to wonder."

"Well, not very much, that was clear," I say.

I am remembering how they both looked so tired and worried, their soot-streaked faces lit by the fire. They were wearing my personal protective gear, my helmet and spare helmet, my firefighting jacket and windbreaker. *My* things. I wanted to rip the stuff off their bodies. Evan was practicing an arrogant sneer and Chris was shivering up against him, trying not to cry, and I was having none of it. None of it.

Maybe I kind of did try to tear the clothes off them, because I kept grabbing and snatching at them, screaming, "What about *them*? Did you think about *them*?" Even though it was Evan I finally got ahold of it was Chris I was asking. I had my face down so my nose was almost touching his. "Did you just forget about them just like that? Or do you not even care?" I'm not even sure if they knew I was talking about the herons—well, Evan would have had no idea. But Chris might have, except that he was so scared he was actually trembling. Not even that stopped me, not one whit.

"Not one of my best moments," I repeat to Ray, shaking my head. My tone's different; I've let the story get away from me. I even feel a weird tremor in my chest, a shaking I'm afraid will spread. I take a deep breath, try to calm myself.

"And you know how the rest of it goes," I add lamely. "The charges, the penalties. What we decided to do, because we had to do something, and then Social Services getting involved. The whole huge mess."

My heart is pounding and I look out the window at the miserable rain, think how for most people it would be the burning that brings back that ash-choked night. For me it's the sodden piss of water on leaves. I'm wishing I'd kept my mouth shut.

Ray clears his throat. He says, "Actually, that was the part I was asking about. How that all happened. Because. Well, because."

I have a sudden image of the trailer on the evening after Henry beat the boys with his Rodeo Days belt. Henry sat in front of the TV with a plate of peas and hot dogs, eyes fixed on the screen but not watching, not responding. I ate my dinner alone at the dining room table. Through the closed door to his room I could actually hear Evan's complete and total scorn; I could also hear the miserable little sobs of Chris. I suppose this was where an intelligent person, a sensitive person, would have done something. But for some reason I thought it would all blow over, that we'd get over it, like we always had. Or else I thought it was already too late. I don't know. That day is kind of a blur, and all I can really conjure up is how the hot dogs felt as big as horse pills going down my throat.

"Henry kept asking me, what should I do, what should I do?" I say, hating the way my voice is husky. "I said, I don't know. They're your boys."

Chris those days not even looking at me, not meeting my eye. Sulking, I thought. That was the other thing: all the old roles and alliances were broken. Maybe I was in it just as deep as Henry, only I would never admit it. Have never admitted it.

"Henry'd just keep pestering me. Should we do this, should we do that? Trying out all these ideas, like he was asking for my permission or something." That was how we worked, I want to explain.

I go on. My imitation Henry voice has gotten clumsy, bitter-sounding. "'*On the one hand it was an accident,*' he'd say. '*They were just playing with your fire gear.*' '*On the other hand that equipment isn't a toy,*' he'd answer himself. '*And they ought to know that by now. Mistakes have consequences, that's something I've got to teach them. They're just these irresponsible little punks right now. It's goddamn embarrassing.*'"

God, how he was pissing me off. This thing, that thing, what should we do. When all I thought was that it wouldn't matter either way—whatever he did would ignite the blow-up, and then we could wait awhile, and then things would go back to normal. The thing was, I was telling myself all along that it was Henry who had to make the first move. I say, "I just got sick of all Henry's dither-dathering. So in the end I was like, go for it."

Ray nods. Thoughtfully. Pretty far cry from your own little home, I want to say, but obviously don't. I want to ask him what he would have done, on the odd chance his honor-roll kids went out and torched three snowplows and a wildlife refuge. I want to say, okay, we've had our little heart-to-heart, let's move on.

He brushes some crumbs off his lap, straightens up. "Did you ever find out who told Social Services?" he asks.

It's a question that takes me by surprise. "Well, the boys, we always thought," I say. It wasn't something Henry and I ever talked about. But the boys weren't exactly shy about parading their welts around to any and all that asked, although come to think of it, the only ones I knew for sure to have asked them were Social Services, and then later the Judge. I remember suddenly how for a while I had a weird suspicion that it was Henry who'd turned himself in, because of the way he just let everything happen after that. He didn't even put up a fight when Darlene, his ex, called collect from Florida to tell him she was going to sue for full custody.

Something in Ray's face changes as he says, "It was a strange time, then. Lee Hale was on leave that month, you remember. So it was just Henry and me down in that basement office. And he was muttering things, muttering and muttering. I never knew what to make of it and then you weren't talking either, wouldn't say nothing to nobody..."

"I was trying to stay out of it," I say, my voice a little louder than it needs to be.

"Well, I didn't know what was going on. And it turned out the day I picked to go down and talk to the boys was I guess just the day or so after. After Henry. And when I saw all those bruises and then tried to confront Henry—things just got out of hand."

It's like I know what Ray is trying to say and I don't want to hear it. I lean down and turn on the truck so that we can go somewhere, anywhere, get out of this conversation. I figure we better get down past that tight spot in the road before the roads really get soft and I probably say something like this to Ray. In any case he doesn't seem to have any objection to what we're doing. In fact he's still over there talking, even though I can barely hear him over the noise of the engine and the squeal of the branches taking off our paint.

This is what it sounds like he's saying: "Of course they asked me when I filed the report whether I thought you all posed any danger to the boys. And I don't know. I didn't know what to tell them. So I said I didn't know. Said I didn't think so but I didn't know."

We pull out onto the road and it is greasy. Slick as snot, as we like to say. I'm more cautious than on the way up and I stop to make sure I've got it in four-wheel drive low. No need to rush this, I tell myself, although my toe keeps fluttering the gas a little too hard.

And let me tell you, Ray is not exactly helping. Blabbity blabbity blab. It's like he's had this confession up his sleeve all winter and was just waiting for the perfect moment. "And then when I talked to the boys," he's saying now. "I kept telling myself this. And then when Henry started having his doubts I knew I had to do something."

"Henry had his doubts?" I ask, not even thinking about it. The rain's really coming down and I'm starting to wonder if we shouldn't pull over and wait for the roads to dry out a bit before trying the safety stand-down curve. I have a sudden sense of what it will feel like as the wheels lose their grip on the road, as the clutch gives up and we start sliding down.

"You remember how Henry was after that first week. Going around the office telling everyone he didn't think you were fit parents, that maybe once you were but now you weren't. He kept saying, Something has broken, something has broken." I can sense Ray looking at me while he talks, waiting for me to nod in agreement. I can't agree because I don't remember any of this. Henry never said more than two words to me after he hit the boys.

"I knew it," I say. "Henry had a breakdown."

"Nancy, what Henry said is that he'd always thought you kind of loved the boys. In your phone-it-in way. That's how he put it. Phone-it-in way." His rueful laugh makes me jump. "But then after you just didn't do anything, after you just let him—well, he said he didn't know any more. He said it seemed like Evan and Chris could have been any two kids, for all you seemed to care. Whatever he thought the family was built on, he said, was false. And there wasn't any more point to any of it."

Here we are at the curve. I stop the truck. "What?" I say.

"Now I think he might have been over-harsh," Ray keeps going, picking at his cuticles nervously. "But at the time, with everything that was going on—well, I wasn't sure. I just wasn't sure."

I open the door before he can lean forward and say anything more in that earnest voice of his. I get out into the rain, saying that I just have to check the road. The rain plasters my hair to my head, my boots thicken with mud, and I see that we couldn't possibly have made it. At least this is what I think I see. It's as if I notice for the first time how incredibly narrow this stretch is, how it seems I could span it with my outstretched arms and I'm sure I couldn't do the same for the truck body. But there is no crumbling, no washout, nothing to show that the road is any different than it's ever been. But it's obvious to me we're going to have to walk out.

I feel light-headed and nauseous, have to lay my hand on the truck's hood to steady myself. Have to lay my forehead on the hood, too, the steaming gritty surface not quite a comfort. I'm furious at my shaking legs. Bad roads are nothing and we're fine, we stopped in time, we'll be able to get out of this just fine. I'm trying not to think about the last time I saw the boys, getting into the truck the morning Henry took them to the airport to send them on their way to Florida. Chris looked so small, the hood of his sweatshirt almost too big for his head. He looked back at the trailer one last time, his face blank and desperate; as he met my eyes I saw his face lift with a sudden something—hopefulness? fear? regret?—and I stepped back from the window, out of his line of sight, as if I hadn't noticed.

Ray opens his door. "You all right?"

I wonder if throwing up would be a satisfactory answer.

"I am not fine, Ray McCallum. I am not fine," I say, finally. I am trying not to think about the things I could have done.

I am trying not to think about what I did not do.

I am trying not to think about the bare apartment I will return to in a few hours, where I will strip off my gear, my sodden jeans and my mud-caked boots, my rain slicker and my rain-soaked shirt and my sweat-soaked bra, with Bette frolicking desperately around my feet. Where I will run the hot water in the shower until the mirror steams up and the great miserable hulk of myself has disappeared and I will not have to look at this great beast breaking down in gusty sobs because the whole great world she had thought she had was gone, forever, gone.

I don't wait for Ray to pull together his things, for him to gather whatever items he thinks are prudent and necessary. I start walking, the mud-caked soles of my boots making a slight sucking sound at each step. By the time I get to the burnline I'm alone, one woman lumbering through the smoldering mess. I don't hear the purr of the truck until it's almost upon me and Ray's leaning out the driver's side window saying, "Get in. Nancy, for Godssakes, get in."

The Nimrod Literary Awards
The Pablo Neruda Prize for Poetry

Semi-Finalist
Davis McCombs

Not Untwist

The fescue stretched to the door of the white farmhouse
and a cold sun hammered planks of light onto the barn
and on a clump of tilted outbuildings. I drove that plunging road
all winter, past the old farm and the boundary fence
where three hogs' heads had been nailed to a board.
They stared with their withering eyes at the road
and the skin shrank away from their teeth and blackened.
I didn't think of them except in those moments, rounding
the turn and coming up over grass, when they were before me.
Wind whined through their ribs of wire and each day
shriveled down to the hill's bitter dark and the block of light
from the window where the old farmer must have sat,
asleep in front of the television. Something about the place
troubled me—if only fitfully and only vaguely. Yes,
something was happening there or about to happen.
It trembled in the dry chickweed under the fence or waited
where the barn strained its wedge of shadow toward the pond.
Once, I saw the old man, thin as a stalk, climbing up into the seat
of an ancient tractor. I didn't wave. I didn't stop and take it in,
and then the morning, pale and warm, the car lifting over
the seedheads, when I saw the grass charred nearly to the fence,
a heap of ash still trickling smoke where the house had stood.

THE NIMROD LITERARY AWARDS

The Pablo Neruda Prize for Poetry

SEMI-FINALIST

JUDITH PACHT

A Cumulus Fiction vi.

Lightning flash—
what I thought were faces
are plumes of pampas grass.
—Basho

稲妻や顔のところが薄の穂

Lightning: white heat or a weightless
flash—a sudden load lifted.
What lies between the two?
I am suspended, hanging, no
thought of time. 2 AM, soft-boil an egg as if it
were morning. It feels safe this way. Those white hot
faces, simply paper poppies, fragments blowing sideways
are only my constructions, fires bursting into
plumes into nothing at all. Collisions
of nothingness only in my head. I say, inside fear lies freedom,
pampas grass does swing easily in the breeze, cut
grass is simply grass cut, the scent earthy, the soil wet & sweet.

I Knew a Little Later

By then it was winter
the hard moon in the window

The wind in all
its whiteness
the oak a blowing silhouette

Your boots
on the long stairs

raw sound
slipping past mirrors

I no longer sleep
I have so little to tell you

The door opens gradually
but you never arrive

I run out in my nightshirt
all I can see are trees dismantling

The edges, little ghosts
your thinness like a blade

Away

A great stillness falls on the house & fills up
the litter she left & a bareness descends

for me to order: my mission is to range the bones
with some precision she would mock if she knew

about it happening: me standing in the middle of:
wringing my hands: the disorder, *desmadre* of gone

so now it's the towels in disarray & water too, still,
on the floor, the space where her clothes were, the square

of her vanished computer, dedusted,
I must cope with, so onto them; & in the spaces

in between I try stacking things on top
of the nothing: new soap in the tray

Christopher Woods, photograph

FINALIST

ZANE KOTKER

Stand and Pivot

The nurses say he can't go home.
He can't go home because he cannot
stand and pivot. Stand and what? I ask,
as if it means to dance with all expenses paid
at Mardi Gras. "He has to show that he can stand
on his good leg, balance, and turn," a nurse explains.
"Or how will he get himself from bed to chair?"
How indeed, though stand and pivot's not a skill
we ever knew we had.
So off to rehab where
Eileen will help. She calls him Hon and orders
him to "move that tushy, mister," tells him he's
making her do all the work. "Come on, Hon,
this is a two-way street. It's you and me."
But he can't recapture what he's lost and we're
dismissed. Sent home alone, together.

Come, my friend,
my long looked-for love, we'll stand and pivot
all we want, we'll boogaloo the whole night
through. Just you and me. Just me and you.

If You're Choking, I'm to Go on Eating

As with falling, you forbid all help.
No shoulder thump, no Heimlich. You'll be fine.
We sit at table by the window looking past
our pale azaleas to the neighbor's perfect lawn.
I'm thinking I might mention how the Great Ones
sat at table over the Euphrates long ago:
Lord Sky nose deep in chickpea soup
Lord Waters slopping up the beer
Lord Air winking at my Lady Earth
who shows a bit of leg beneath her chair.
But you begin to gasp and choke
so I say none of that and go on eating
as you've instructed me. Not standing
when you gasp for air, not rushing
to your side, just sipping a bit of wine,
just forking a little pasta, until you're
back to breath when I may say,
"Are you okay?" And you reply, "I'm fine."

The Bad News Room

While you lie in coma, eyes half-shut,
the doctor calls us to the bad news room
with its soft chairs and specious greens.
He tells us of the talks he's had with you
—no fancy stuff, just morphine, please—
then turns to me, the proxy, asks,
Shall we insert a feeding tube? No, I say,
because we, too, have talked of this. I turn
to check for family unanimity: okay, okay.

The doctor moves to question two, Shall we
continue then with the hydration? Water?
No water? We never spoke of water!
Am I to let you cross the desert parched,
craving, wild for water? He won't be thirsty,
the doctor notes, not with the morphine
we'll be giving him. So I say no, no water
and I empty out your cup.

FINALIST
MICHELLE COLLINS ANDERSON

Cancer (& Other Unforgivable Curses)

I got the note in Esmé's backpack this afternoon: her long black cape has become "a distraction to the class" and she is no longer welcome to wear it to school. There was no mention of the wand. It is difficult to be a wizard among "Muggles"—your average, run-of-the-mill human beings. Just as I am finding it difficult to be human when I would gladly summon magic or pray for miracles.

Justin is with the hospice nurse now. She is checking his vital signs, making notes, checking the log of medications—the amounts, the times given—that I keep so meticulously, my letters curling around the white spaces of the chart. Soon she will bathe him, a sponge bath that will clean away the perspiration but will not erase the yellow of his skin. She will let me do the shampooing and the shaving: I insist. Justin was not—is not—a vain man, but he did love his hair. It is thick and black and edged with gray; he liked to keep it just the slightest bit long, which gave him the rumpled professor look I love. He is an artist, a painter, but made his living as the creative director at a local ad agency—overseeing all the words and images that go into ads and commercials and websites. He is what they call a "creative guru," a "big idea" man: he sees forest, not trees; constellations rather than stars.

He was diagnosed just seven months ago. Pancreatic cancer. It was what my O.R. nurse friend, Julie, called a classic "peek-and-shriek": the surgeons opened him up to see what was going on inside and promptly sewed him back together and sent him home to die. Julie doesn't mean to be macabre or insensitive. I think she simply forgets that most of us don't see this every day.

The sound Justin makes when he breathes now is a like a percolating coffee pot, the kind my parents had on the farm. Similarly, he is boiling hot and bringing things up to the top, like the foamy yellow-brown spittle that needs to be swabbed regularly from the insides of his mouth. Julie says that means we are getting toward the end.

Sometimes I hate Julie. That know-it-all bitch.

"Esmé," I call up the stairs.

"Yes, Mummy."

Esmé has the most adorable British accent—which I only mention because we are not British. We are Americans. Midwesterners. Missourians. We do not take tea and crumpets, although we do love our sweetened iced tea and just saying the word "crumpet" is somehow altogether satisfying. Perhaps it is the English in my blood, from my grandmother on my mother's side. Or maybe it is because I am a librarian who cannot help delighting in the way a word can feel in my mouth.

"May I speak with you for a moment?"

"Certainly," she says.

I hear the clomp of her black boots before I see her at the top of the staircase. She is a vision in her black skirt, white oxford shirt and tie—the latter two nearly obscured by the cape, which is tied in large, childish loops at her throat. Her magenta cat-eye eyeglass frames—while not standard-issue black circles like Harry Potter's—nonetheless sport a scroll of masking tape at the bridge, like the young wizard's in Book One. Her glasses are not broken. She waves her wand at me. It is a replica of Harry's, which—I should not admit to knowing—is precisely eleven inches, made from holly, and contains a single phoenix feather. Esme's is molded plastic—no feather—but quite realistic.

"Hi, Mum."

"Hi, darling. How was your Monday?"

"Oh," she pauses before making her way down. "Decidedly unmagical."

She is only eight, but her vocabulary is what the teachers label as "well above grade level," as are her reading and writing skills. I will credit J. K. Rowling where credit is due, despite my professional distaste for her excessive reliance on "l-y" adverbs. Esmé has read the entire Harry Potter series of seven books seven times through and is about to finish round eight. She started in kindergarten, when the heft of a Harry Potter book in her backpack could nearly tip her over.

"I'm sorry to hear that," I say. I raise an eyebrow. "Is there anything you'd like to tell me?"

Her small face is pensive, surrounded by a curly brown mane of hair—my hair—more Hermione Granger than Harry Potter, but she refuses to be swayed. It is Harry whom she loves; Harry she pretends to be.

"Not in particular."

"I've gotten a note that says your cape is a distraction."

Esmé sighs. "It's a *cloak*."

"Cloak, then. So?"

"Muggles," she says finally. "They've no imagination."

"Have you considered that perhaps you have a bit too much of one?"

Esmé treats me to her newly perfected pre-teen eye roll. "Mummy," she says, exasperated. "Listen to yourself. There's no such thing as too much imagination. You've said so yourself. Besides," she adds, almost as an afterthought, "I neutralized my spell on Rebecca as soon as Mrs. Warson asked me to."

"Spell?"

"I had to put a *Silencio* on her," Esme says. "She talks too much. Chatters away, really. I think even Mrs. Warson felt relieved someone had taken her in hand."

"But...?"

Esmé shrugs.

"Mrs. Reece?" The nurse is calling me. Back to my duties.

"We will talk more about this, Esmé," I say. "But no more cloak. No more wand. And for heaven's sake, you must stop cursing people."

"Spells, Mummy. They are spells," she says indignantly. "I would never put a curse on anyone. That would be *unforgivable."*

* * *

Esmé is right, of course. I should know my wizarding lore from all the hours of Harry Potter I have read to her at bedtime. The young wizards at Hogwarts School of Witchcraft and Wizardry learn all sorts of spells—and how to use them responsibly. But the dark wizards—the Death Eaters—have no such scruples. They would not hesitate to employ one of the "Unforgivable Curses," of which there are three:

• The *Cruciatus* curse inflicts unbearable pain on its recipient. Much like, say, a very aggressive, untreatable form of cancer.

• The *Imperius* curse causes the victim to follow any and all commands of the curse-caster. A victim of this curse experiences total release from responsibility for any actions, at the cost of free will. Such victimhood, in my current circumstances, has much more appeal than I care to admit.

• And the third, the *Avada Kedavra* curse, is also known as the "killing curse" because it causes instant, painless death in its intended victim.

Now that I ponder it, is that last curse truly so unforgivable? My last few weeks with Justin may have convinced me otherwise. Imagine: an incantation. A wave of a wand. And poof! No more pain.

But no more person, either.

That is the caveat to *Avada Kedavra:* there is no counterspell, no means of blocking it. It is irreversible. Irrevocable.

Forever.

* * *

It is time to begin our goodbyes, the nurse says. Robin. Her eyes are gray and wise. She eases the blanket back from Justin's feet and ankles to show me the violet mottling under the golden sheen of his jaundice. She mentions the percolating, too.

"But he is so warm," I say. "Not cold at all. His hands and feet."

"His heart is strong," she says. "But his lungs are filling up." For the first time I notice the worry lines in her face. She takes my hand and runs my fingertips along Justin's closed lids, fringed with long, dark eyelashes. Nothing happens.

"Just two days ago, he would blink or twitch when we did that. Remember?"

I nod.

"He is in a coma now," she says softly. "It's time to make some calls."

I hear part of me telling her I will do it. But part of me is somewhere else, hovering just beyond my body, her body, and his. Watching. As if this were someone else's drama, someone else's life.

"Mrs. Reece?" She summons me back.

"Evelyn," I say, for the umpteenth time. The intimacy she has shared with my husband, with our family, makes formality seem ridiculous.

"Evelyn. One more thing: you need to tell Justin that it's okay for him to go."

"I know," I say simply. Yet I cannot imagine how I will do this.

"He can still hear you," she says. "Talk to him. And touch him."

"I will," I say. "I do."

* * *

"I do."

When I said those words at our wedding nearly thirteen years ago, I was crossing my fingers beneath my bouquet.

Justin and I met in St. Louis and decided to get married there in the lovely little Lutheran church where I had been baptized as a baby. My parents had lived in the city early in their marriage, before my dad gave in to his yearning for small-town life. So although I wasn't a member at Hope—or anywhere else, to be honest—I liked having that small connection to the church. I was in my first year as a librarian in the downtown branch of the public library, after receiving my master's; Justin lived and worked in St. Louis, too. We both had friends there. A city wedding made more sense than having everyone traipse down to the tiny Ozarks town where I grew up and had only my mother and one ancient set of grandparents remaining, a place where we couldn't serve beer and wine at the reception or dance without the whiff of scandal.

What we had not counted on—with the caterer already booked, the flowers and tuxedos ordered, the dresses made—was the premarital counseling this conservative church would require. I discovered over the course of these sessions that I was required to "submit" to my new husband, to "obey" him, and would have to promise as much in my vows. I also learned that Justin was to be the "spiritual head of the family."

"Think of it like a mobile," Pastor Lucero said seriously, his dark mustache and beard giving him a look uncannily like Lucifer himself. "God is at the top, of course, with the father pie-plate hanging beneath. Then the mother pie-plate below him, and the children pie-plates hanging under her. If the daddy pie-plate pulls away from God, the entire family goes with him."

"But Justin doesn't even go to church," I said, practically smirking. "In fact, I am not sure he believes in God. How can he be the top pie-plate?"

Justin kicked me gently in the shin.

"Just cross your fingers for the submission part," Justin said after we had escaped the oppressive heat of that tiny office into the cool spring evening. "We know what we believe. It's okay. Besides," he winked. "I love it when you're the boss."

So I did. Cross my fingers, I mean. But not for the rest of it: for richer, for poorer, in sickness and in health. 'Til death do us part.

And the whole time I thought I was getting away with something. Avoiding the hard part.

* * *

It is the next day, Tuesday, already. I awake early to the irritated meowing of Justin's old cat, Van Gogh (giant orange tabby, one ear), coming from the kitchen. There I find the poor, cross old thing lying on the counter, writhing and flopping helplessly from side to side, wearing two pairs of handcuffs fashioned from the thick blue rubberbands that typically hold together bunches of broccoli or asparagus. Esmé appears to be poking his face with a pair of tweezers.

"Esmé!"

She whirls around, dropping the tweezers in alarm. But then a cool look remakes itself on her face and she retrieves the silver instrument with one hand, while trying to hold down Van Gogh with the other.

"What on earth are you doing?"

"I just need one long whisker for an elixir," she says, flipping the growling, hissing mound of fur onto its other side. I pity him and his de-clawed paws. "Hold still, Van Gogh!"

"*Elixir?* Esmé! Stop that right this minute!"

With a horrible *thunk,* Van Gogh rolls off the counter and onto the kitchen floor. Handcuffed cats do not, for the record, land on their feet.

"But it's for Daddy." Esmé juts her chin out.

"Daddy has all the medicines he needs."

"Then why aren't they *working?*"

I find myself unable to explain how Justin's medications aren't for healing, but rather for amelioration, for relief. "Symptom management," the doctor had called it. The cancer gets to do whatever it likes. Manage *this,* I think, mentally flipping off that physician who had sat so casually in his neat white coat amid the beeping, blinking ICU monitors. I hustle Esmé upstairs to brush her teeth while I set a highly agitated Van Gogh free. The look he gives me over his shoulder as he walks away is one of utter and complete disgust. I envy his freedom, his ability to disappear beneath a bed or in the back of a closet until it is safe or desirable to come out.

After the cat incident, I send a cape-free Esmé off to school, but somewhat reluctantly. Is it better to hold on to some shred of normalcy—although how normal can it be to go to school with your dad dying in your front room?—or to shuck routine and just embrace this time for what it is: a vigil? I have decided this will be her last day, that having her out of the house today will enable me to make those phone calls. To get ready for the onslaught. Justin's parents, his brother, my mom. His boss, my boss. His friends, our friends. Neighbors. My best friend, Julie, whom I have already mentioned.

I do not hate her. She is not really a bitch.

But a know-it-all? Absolutely.

It occurs to me that this will be almost like having a wedding in reverse. All our loved ones gathering to witness a dissolution, a breaking of the earthly bonds. There will be tears, prayers, and flowers. Organ music. Suits and dresses. Tons of food.

No dancing. Although I think Justin would encourage dancing.

They have all been with me throughout Justin's illness, of course. My mom and his parents and his brother have taken turns these last few weeks, ever since Justin was hospitalized after collapsing in the kitchen and we decided a few days later to bring him home on hospice. I just sent them away, actually, three days ago. I needed a break from all the bodies in the house, the morose faces, the helpless hands. The constant need to think about what people might want or need to eat, even as Justin stopped eating altogether. I needed some time alone with just him and Esmé.

Early last week he could still talk a little, although I could tell it exhausted him. He could still hold me when I climbed into the hospital bed we had ordered for him and set up in the living room along with the oxygen machine. It was—it is—his favorite room: shelves full of his art books and my substantial fiction collection (alphabetized, of course), walls hung with his paintings, the brick fireplace, our family photos, a comfy camelback couch, the floor-to-ceiling windows. He loved the light. In the evenings, he would light the dozen or more pillar candles of varying heights that decorate our mantel. There is something about candlelight, Justin said, that is kind to paintings and human faces. It was a ritual: he used a bottle of butane to fill the heavy silver lighter inscribed with his grandfather's initials, then carefully attended to each wick. This is where we read, together, after dinner and homework were through. Sometimes Van Gogh deigned to join us.

Justin even managed, just a few short days ago, to lie waiting, patiently and expectantly, as Esmé cast a host of spells in her efforts to make him better or different or someone else entirely.

"Just call me Dumbledore," Justin said, reaching for her small, be-caped body.

"No, Daddy. You can't be Dumbledore. He is old and gray with a tremendously long beard," she said seriously. "And he dies in Book Six."

Justin and I tried not to look at each other.

"Lord Voldemort, then?"

"Too evil."

"Snape?"

"Well, you *do* have the same black hair. But he's creepy, Dad. Plus, he dies in Book Seven."

"Esmé!" My voice came out sharp, a warning.

"Well, he *does.*"

Justin seemed nonplussed. "Hagrid, then."

Esmé smiled, pleased. "A giant, Dad? Really?"

"A giant who loves animals, magical creatures, and above all, Harry Potter." Justin squeezed her tight. "And who doesn't always know the right thing to say."

Here he looked at me. I shrugged. Me, either.

Now I check the oxygen tank and give Justin his litany of medications. Esmé calls them his "potions." The Ativan for anxiety. The Atropine to dry up the goo in his lungs. The Roxanol for pain. The Haldol for agitation. There are drops and pills I grind up and mix in a liquid that can be drawn into a tiny syringe, something I can slip between his teeth and cheek while I hold his chin to make sure it all goes down. I tell Justin everything I am doing, everything I will do.

I love you, Justin. But I would be lying if I said I'm not a little pissed off.

I reach for one of the special caps Robin has left me and take it out of its wrapper. It is a shower cap of sorts, which I microwave for a minute or two and then secure to Justin's head, tucking in all that unruly hair. I massage the cap and soon lather builds up, seeping from beneath the edge of the elastic band. Afterwards, I remove the cap, towel his hair and comb it. Not as good as a real shampoo, but it will do. Marvelous inventions they have for the infirm and dying these days. The shaving is a bit trickier—there is no microwavable substitute for shaving cream and straight-edge. But I manage.

The phone rings. Justin's mom? Or mine? I am not quite ready for what I am supposed to say today.

But the number is local. The school.

"Mrs. Reece?"

"Yes?"

"This is Mrs. Warson from the elementary school. Esmé's teacher?"

"Of course. Is something wrong?"

"Well. . ." There is one of those silences. "I'm afraid Esmé is still wearing her cape today. And as I had mentioned in my note yesterday. . ."

"Yes, I got the note and spoke with Esmé about it. She understood that she was not to wear it to school anymore."

"I am afraid she hid it beneath her fleece jacket this morning. All balled up. She looked like a little hunchback. I am surprised you didn't notice."

Ouch: the inattentive mom zinger. So that's how she wants to play it. But I see your politically incorrect hunchback reference and raise you one "C" word.

"Well, we are both dealing with the small matter of her father's *cancer*," I say, allowing only the tiniest bit of snark to creep into my voice. "I'm sure you understand."

"Yes. Oh, yes, I'm so sorry. I hate to even bring this up at all."

"But?"

"It seems she has cast several spells on her classmates," says Mrs. Warson. "She silenced Rebecca yesterday and then this morning she put a freezing spell on Jorge."

"That's ridiculous."

"Well, I know it *sounds* ridiculous, but the fact is, Rebecca still will not say a word and Jorge has not moved from his chair. Not even for recess."

"What? Is this some kind of joke?"

"I wish it were, Mrs. Reece. But I honestly don't know what to do. The other children seem a bit afraid of Esmé."

"She is an eight-year-old girl. She weighs barely fifty pounds—"

"She is in the principal's office right now," Mrs. Warson interjects. "You should probably come and get her."

I start to say something extremely unkind. But what would that accomplish?

"Expelliarmus," I say instead. This is the most expedient way to disarm a witch.

"Excuse me?"

"I'll be there as soon as I can."

A knock on the door of our Dutch colonial, with its barn-shaped dusty blue second story atop the cool, gray-white limestone of the first. It is Margie. One half of Margie-and-Tom, our across-the-street neighbors. They have one son, Griffin, who is eleven. He and Esmé used to play together until fairly recently, when it became uncool for either of them to associate with the other gender.

"Hey, there," Margie's eyes are already welling up. "How is Justin?"

"Not too good," I say. Her tears seem to harden rather than soften me. "Coma."

"Oh, Evelyn!" She throws her arms around me and I let her hold me, although I can't seem to hold her back. I am stiff, like a papoose strapped to a board. But unable to allow myself to be carried on someone's back. She wipes her eyes with the sleeve of her windbreaker. It is spring. The fact of it surprises me every time I step outside: all the bursting colors and unfurling green life everywhere. It hurts my eyes.

I lead her into the living room, show her how to shift Justin with pillows if he seems uncomfortable. Write down my cellphone number. Point out the hospice number, just in case. *Just in case.* Justin's case. A hopeless case.

"I'll be right back," I say. "Fifteen minutes."

"Take your time," she says. "Take all the time you need."

It would not matter if I had hours or days. Esmé does not want to talk.

In my rearview mirror, I see her staring out the window, avoiding my gaze. Her face is swollen and blotchy, although she was not crying when I picked her up. I have told the principal I will be keeping Esmé home until things settle down.

"Of course," he said. "I'm sorry. But I understand completely. We all do."

I nodded, all the while herding Esmé out of his office and through the heavy steel double doors of the school. The playground smelled of sun-warmed earth and cedar mulch and was full of running, boisterous children. I am finding it difficult to remember what is normal, what kinds of things go on out here in the world.

"Esmé," I say. "Look at me."

She refuses. Her hands in her lap are balling and unballing her black cape. We drive in silence, with just the hum of the motor and the occasional bump from the street beneath. In the driveway, I turn off the engine and it makes a metallic pinging as it cools.

"Esmé," I finally say. "Daddy may not be with us much longer."

I turn to meet her eyes. They are hazel like Justin's. The color of surprise.

"Where is he going?"

It is a terrible thing to break down in front of your child. I remember my father crying exactly once: when his mother died. That scared me far more than my grandma's shrunken, lifeless body at the funeral. She didn't look like someone I knew. But my father crying? He looked the same, but I did not know that man at all.

Esmé has climbed into the front seat and hands me a paper napkin embossed with McDonald's arches. I swipe at the tears and snot coalescing at the bottom of my face.

"Daddy is dying, sweetheart."

"I know. But where will he go?"

"I don't know," I say. The yard is practically pulsing with purple crocuses, brilliant yellow jonquils, the bottlebrush blooms of lavender hyacinths.

"When Dumbledore died, Harry could still talk to him inside his head," Esmé says. She shoves open the car door.

"Maybe it will be like that," I say. But the door is slamming, and the only one I am left trying to convince is myself.

* * *

Inside the house, Margie tells me that everything is "perfectly fine." I never knew what an ironic world I lived in until Justin became so sick. Or perhaps it is just that one's definition of words such as "perfect" and "fine" change in relation to the circumstances in which one finds oneself. All of which is to say: if everything here is perfectly fine, I would hate to see the alternative.

I want to stop thinking so much. But my librarian self cannot help noticing how words can be so impotent and meaningless and yet, at the same time, absolutely loaded. I am horrified by how pedestrian, how unexalted my thoughts are at a time like this. I don't know *how* to think anymore, how to be in my own skin. But then, I suppose, this is my first dying husband. I should cut myself some slack. Everything is *perfectly fine.*

Margie promises to send over chicken soup. I say thank you.

It is too much trouble to tell her about our freezer, already filled to bursting with donated casseroles assembled from chicken, Campbell's Cream of Mushroom soup, and crushed stale potato chips. If I felt like eating—which I don't—I might die of a heart attack or an artery-clog-induced stroke. Who knew food could be so beige? Esmé and I eat one-dish meals around Justin's bed: popcorn or a bowl of ice cream or cold cereal. Still beige, but so much yummier somehow. It feels like we are camping out, like this is just temporary. Like we will return to regular programming soon.

"We're thinking about you," Margie says at the door. She hesitates a second and grasps one of my hands in hers. "We're praying for you all, Evelyn."

I know she is putting herself out there to say this. We are the non-churchgoers on the block. The Sunday layabouts. The agnostics. The daddy pie-plate has swung wide and taken us far from the fold.

"Thank you, Margie," I say. "It means a lot."

* * *

Robin is here already. The day has disappeared, shadows falling. She was coming every few days, but told me yesterday that she will come every day now until the end.

"I didn't expect to find you and Esmé alone," she says pointedly but gently.

Esmé likes Robin, who shows her lots of little tricks to help make her father more comfortable. Like dipping the small, stiff swabs in water before use so that they are softer inside his mouth. Or putting Vaseline around the rims of both nostrils where the oxygen tubes chafe. A bit of lip balm on his cracked, flaking mouth.

"I had some things come up," I say. I laugh at how preposterous that sounds. As if anything could trump the drama in my living room. *Things have come up.* A comeuppance? "But I'll call while you're here."

"Atta girl."

* * *

"Nancy," I say, when Justin's mom picks up. They are in Indianapolis, only five hours away, but our connection sounds as distant as another universe.

"Oh, God. Evelyn." She puts a hand over the phone. "Paul? Paul! It's Evelyn."

"Is everything okay?" A twinge of hope yet in her voice, but mostly fear.

"Yes," I say. "I mean, no. He's alive, but the nurse says it won't be long now."

"We'll get right in the car," says Paul, his gruff voice extra loud on the extension.

"No, no need of that," I say. I am not ready. Give me just one more night, I think. Please. "Just pack and get things in order. Tomorrow will be perfectly fine."

Perfectly fine. Did I really just say that?

"We never should have left." Nancy is sobbing. "Are you sure, Evelyn?"

"Yes, I'm sure." No, I am not. But I push on, asking them to call Justin's brother, Jake. Before we hang up, they assure me that they love us all so very much.

"Me, too," I say.

After I hang up, my hand rests heavily on the handset. It is so exhausting to talk. Punching in numbers, connecting with someone I love—who loves Justin, too—to talk about *disconnecting* from this life, this person we all care about. I lie down, paralyzed.

Is there any place lonelier than a double bed you used to share with someone? I realize I have not slept here in weeks. That, in fact, I have not slept here since Justin fell. I have slept, of course. But not much—and mostly on the living room couch.

Even though I knew in the back of my mind that there would be a last time we slept together, I thought I would recognize it happening in the moment. A flashing neon sign or a message in marquee lights, perhaps. Or at a minimum—and this sounds absurd—I imagined soft lights, gentle touches, Brahms in the background. Instead, I helped Justin up the stairs and he was so exhausted he just lay there while I undressed him and drew up his blankets. The whole thing made him so angry, so disgusted with himself—with his cancer—that he lashed out: "Don't touch me, goddamnit!" Then he turned his back to me—no goodnight kiss, nothing—and slept fitfully all night, facing the wall.

The next morning he fell in the kitchen and, suddenly, we had already spent our last night in our bed. It was in the past. And we hadn't even known it was happening.

"Mrs. Reece?" Robin pokes her head in to let me know she is leaving.

"Evelyn," I reply, staring up at her from my prone position on the bed.

"How are the calls coming?"

"One down."

She frowns. "Can someone else help? Justin's time may be short."

"Short." I repeat the word without really assimilating its meaning. I have never associated this word with Justin before, either in height or temperament.

Justin is short on time. *A short-timer.*

"A few days at most," she says. "I'm sorry. You may have noticed that his breathing has gotten more shallow. There's no urine output, either."

She is right. It has been two days since I emptied the plastic pouch of dark gold liquid hanging from his bed. "His kidneys are shutting down," she says.

"My nurse friend, Julie," I say. "She'll know what to tell everyone."

Robin smiles. "We nurses don't always know what to say," she says. "But we usually know what to do. Do you want me to call her for you?"

I hand her the phone. Robin's end of the conversation sounds more like a soothing flow of music than distinct words. She gives me the phone back. Nods.

"Hi, Jules," I say. "I am sorry. I couldn't seem to dial the damn phone."

"Oh, Evelyn. Oh, baby," she says. "I'm the one who's sorry. I should've called earlier. I'll tell them all to come tomorrow. And I'll be over first thing to check on you."

"You don't need to do that."

"Evelyn," she says firmly. "Let me help you. I can do this."

"Okay," I say, my throat closing over a painful sob. I am relieved. I do not hate her anymore for her competence. For understanding what all of this means.

"Hang in there, baby," she says. I flash on a poster I had at Esmé's age: the darling tabby kitten dangling from a branch, eyes desperate, claws dug in. *Hang on, baby. Friday's coming.*

Robin helps me up. "I'll let myself out. Wash your face, okay?"

"Yes," I say. "I will."

"Justin's stable right now," she says. "But there's a little girl down there who needs you."

* * *

From the top of the stairs I can see that the living room is dark but for a small bedside lamp beside Justin. His face looks more relaxed than it has in days. The oxygen machine in the corner gives the house a womblike hum. Everything is so still.

But then a small movement catches my eye: there, in front of the fireplace with her small, cloaked back to me, is Esmé. She is mumbling something, words that I cannot quite make out. I take another step closer, stealthily, not wanting to interrupt. I understand that she is summoning someone or something, perhaps making some kind of magic for her father. It tears at my heart to see hope so naked, so earnestly and hopelessly employed. And yet I am transfixed by the scene, this simple, genuine act of faith in the very face of death. Envious, even.

Slowly, she brings her arms up from her sides. Her wand is in her right hand. She reaches for something on top of the mantel—a bottle?—and kneels down, pouring its contents onto the trio of decorative white birch logs in the fireplace grate.

"*Incendio!*" Esme says now, loudly.

Too late, I see the silver lighter in her left hand as she bends closer toward the grate, her wand raised high in her right. A tiny click.

"Esmé, no!"

Then there is a bright flash that knocks Esmé back onto her heels, her cape blown open, her arms flung up to her face. Flames flare briefly; a wispy black cloud rolls back into the room and dissipates. My mind panics—there is Esmé, Justin, the oxygen tank—and then I am taking the remaining stairs by threes until I am at Esmé's side.

She stares up at me, her mouth making silent O's, a fish gasping on a riverbank. Her bangs are singed and her eyes open wide behind the smudged lenses of her glasses, wider than seems possible: I realize then that her eyebrows are gone, giving her a look of horrible, perpetual surprise. The flames in the fireplace have died away, leaving the birch logs smirched but whole. There is the smell of burnt hair. The oxygen machine hums on, oblivious. Justin, too, remains unmoved.

"Mama," she whispers, and for a moment, she is no longer British, no longer a wizard. I lift her into my arms, brush aside the sizzled hair at her forehead to reveal a black, lightning-shaped scar near the upper right hairline. I recognize this as the work of a Sharpie, not the result of the fire or a fall or other mishap. How magnificent, I think, to be so clearly marked by suffering. I am frightened that when Justin dies, people will look at me and be unable to see him, too; the ways he marked my life, the ways he changed me. Terrified that he will simply disappear.

I am already having difficulty picturing Justin anywhere but in a hospital bed, any way but jaundiced, wasted. Wordless. Already I can no longer recall exactly the way his eyes looked at me or the smile that always began a bit reluctantly on one side of his mouth—was it the left?—before taking over his entire face.

But there is Esmé, of course. She is right here. I clutch her to my chest and rock her.

* * *

After a bath in which I confirm that both eyebrows and a measure of pride are the only casualties of Esmé's wizardry-gone-wild ("But, Mummy, Harry conferences with other wizards in the fireplace flames all the time—for advice, you know?"), we join Justin in the living room once more while we eat a dinner of toasted frozen pancakes slathered with peanut butter. Esmé is in her footie pajamas and cape at the end of Justin's bed; I pull an armchair closer to the side and lower the metal rail so that I can touch them. I can make out the two flat shining buttons of Van Gogh's wary eyes in the dark beneath the couch.

Soon, Esmé will request Harry Potter and lose herself in Book Seven, the one where Harry dies but doesn't, talks to Dumbledore (his dead mentor who is still available for counsel), vanquishes Voldemort and lives happily ever after. Harry even marries and becomes a parent.

He has no idea what he is in for.

Esmé will eventually fall asleep, curling up around Justin's feet. I will mark her page, gently close her book, smooth her cape and cover her with a soft fleece blanket. I will give Justin his meds, hold his hand, and watch him breathe.

Rennervate, I will whisper.

Reparo, I will plead.

Please, God. Please.

But Justin will not wake up. Justin will not heal.

It's okay, I will say. It is okay for you to go.

They will be here soon, the others. The ones who love Justin, too. They will ring the doorbell and wait politely for me to open the door. Someone will knock. My father-in-law, Paul, perhaps. And then he will knock again, more loudly. They will look at each other and shrug before letting themselves in.

"Knock, knock. Hello? Evelyn? Esmé?"

They will look for us in the living room, moving quickly to Justin's bedside and the rumple of bedclothes and blankets, sheets, pillows, and the clear plastic coils of oxygen tubing. Sunlight will stream through the tall windows. The air will be faintly tinged with the scorch of human hair.

But we will not be there. They will not find us.

We will already be gone. We will have joined hands and said the right words, envisioned ourselves elsewhere. *Disapparated.* Disappeared. We will be flying like Harry Potter, through time and space. Into another universe.

When we land at last, we will tumble, laughing, across some strange terrain. Justin will rise slowly, dusting off his pressed white shirt cuffs, and run his fingers through his thick, tousled hair and grin at me. Esmé will adjust her taped magenta glasses and look around, wonderstruck.

Obliviate, I will say. And everything terrible, everything perfectly fucking fine will fall away, forgotten.

* * *

Later. Much later. My head jerks up from the side of Justin's bed, where I've fallen asleep, resting against his arm. The sky is streaked with light.

Someone is knocking.

* * *

Quickly now. Do not be afraid. Let me take your hand. Ready?

I love you.

Forgive me.

Avada Kedavra!

Silence.

Just the low drone of the oxygen machine and my words echoing off these high-ceilinged walls. Our living room. *The dying room.*

Esmé's eyes are open.

"Mummy." Her voice is a whisper, but it holds a reprimand. "You are just a Muggle."

She pulls herself up until she is seated once more at the foot of Justin's bed. I am still holding his hand. She reaches for his hand, too.

"I know," I say. "I'm sorry."

"It's okay."

We watch Justin's chest go up and then—after what seems a long while—down. His breath is barely audible, his pulse faint. We will keep watching and listening and holding on, spellbound. As long as it takes. Forever.

The knocking again; louder, more insistent.

"Someone is at the door," I say. "We better see who it is."

Eleanor Leonne Bennett, photograph

SEMI-FINALIST

MARSHA TRUMAN COOPER

Suddenly, the blizzard

abated and real snowflakes—
so soft and wet
they felt warm—
began piling deep.

During the Great Depression,
my mother assembled wild
bird eggs for a high school
biology project. She packed
them in typewriter ribbon
boxes, black, on which
she inked each species'
name in golden ink.

I used to peek inside
cotton batting she cut
to enclose her set of robins
or the quail clutch—
blues or speckles
nested and unbroken—
the world excluded
by whiteness and a universe
going silent the instant
I replaced the lid.

But that night when the rough
wind hushed, I dared
to handle a blown-out shell.
Using a collector's drill
and measured breath,
Mother blew her private song
through a single hole,

emptying without shattering
its fragile case. Almost all
the same air, I imagine,
stayed behind inside
just as oceans wait
trapped in a conch spiral.

So if I put my ear close
enough to take out music,
the notes that hold her secrets
can beach with mine
like driftwood cast ashore—
accustomed to the sighs of birds,
the brush of wings,
occasions of protected stillness—
among flakes, the ghosts of feathers,
or shifting dunes.

Katherine Minott, *Death of a Feather,* photograph

Mudflats, Heron

Not one without the other, shimmer of water
where the heron stands, mud dusted
with pollen, a few downy duck feathers,

tracks where the night possum came out
food-searching, found a few
freshwater clams. Cracked shells

lie abandoned here, sucked dry, and there's shit
everywhere, too, green and black
coils from Canada geese.

Why sing of a ravaged spot at the Grand River
needing dredging to clear
silt out, so water will flow?

The whole place tangled and gross with invasive
species—especially purple
loosestrife, that looks elegantly tall

but crowds out bloodroot, spring beauty, the low
ephemerals. In other places,
poison ivy circles cottonwood, sycamore.

The heron lifts off, emits a squawk as sun
smears up full, and boys come
walking, sometimes throwing rocks,

"Can you hit that bird?" I would save her
if I could, my sister beginning
to forget some words and names—

not one without the other, motto
of beauty, of family.
Helpless, now, watching it come.

THE NIMROD LITERARY AWARDS
The Pablo Neruda Prize for Poetry

FINALIST
MELANIE DRANE

from *I Dream of Lost Vocabularies*

The Language Orchard

In memory of Melissa Kimberly Drane
(1959-2013)

Aphasia, from the Greek root word aphatos, *meaning speechless, is an acquired language disorder, often resulting from stroke.*

After the stroke, my sister can't swallow;
I sponge her mouth with water.
She's always struggled to eat—to love
the body's weight, threatening to pull her close
to earth, the scent of pelt, forest, iron-

fruit and underbrush. Clear the small hill
of the pubis, stake the belly with knobs
of bone, turn it into a begging bowl,
and still, a woman's fur grows thick
in places once hairless. Loss rouses feral

instinct; I sleep next to her with one eye
open, listening all night. She's given up
her appetite not just for food, but speech—
now words are hiding all around us
in the soundless dark: hares, voles, soft-

breasted songbirds, breathing rapidly
among the leaves of this abandoned
language orchard, where silver-barked trees
slump with mottled pears, and my hunger
circles—silent, spittle-flecked, and looming.

The Liquid Consistency of Words

How can words flow in this strange place,
where even water has gone stiff?
The nurses label it by thickness: *nectar,*
honey, pudding. How could she name
this stuff, opaque and jellied as glue?
My sister practices blowing kisses
into the mirror, the way the speech therapist
showed her: to rebuild the memory of her face.
When I leave at the end of the day, her eyes
are closed, and she is kissing the air
in the dark over and over and over.
This is how I know she still loves life.

Later, at the Holiday Inn poolside bar, I close
my eyes, drink gin, and kiss the air—
our secret call-and-response since language
fled. What will we imagine, my sister
and I, each alone in our beds tonight,
kissing the air as if words could be seduced?
Our love and tongues are heavy in their beds.
Here, the water is thick as blood.

The Legs of Aging Lawn Chairs

The legs of the aging lawn chairs
on the brick patio are
intertwined   they glow
white in the dark   the chairs
are deep in conversation   talk
far more intimate than their
daytime chat   they are
telling each other then in middle
age you finally accept
that life is not safe
(even as their white legs
safely   reassuringly   intertwine)
they are telling each other
nodding in chair-like agreement
that you finally learn that
real life is made of real risks
and that this knowledge
paradoxically   frees you
frees you   for instance
to sit on the back patio
in all kinds of weather   knowing
a big wind might come and sweep
you down the street   bending
your legs   altering your chair life
forever.
As midnight approaches
the chairs fall silent   then
the big beige chaise leans
forward and suggests they
sing   not something light
like "Tell me Why" or "By the Light
of the Silvery Moon" but something
for this night: "The Fauré Requiem!"
The chairs discuss it   then they
nod and   at a signal
from the chaise   in blessed
chair voices   they take up the

Kyrie   startling sleeping ants
and birds and all the neighbors'
dreams.

Christopher Woods, photograph

FINALIST

JOSEPHINE YU

Middle Class Love Song

When some know-it-all on public radio insists income
    is more hereditary than height or weight, and some other

dour economist agrees we're on the fast track back to serfdom,
    we shrug, so yeah, maybe everybody's broke, but not too broke

to catch a matinee at Miracle 8 or grab a venti from Starbucks,
    and ok, our rental looks kinda trashy, the jasmine vine dying

on the chain-link in a gothic brown tangle—poisoned, we think,
    by our duplex neighbor's latest crazy ex—but we're rich in

monkey grass, which spreads so wildly that the neighbor's kid
    just mows it into a verdant stubble, and we may not have

tidy box hedges or a golf cart to tootle down the street in,
    like the doctor in the McMansion next door, his two yellow

labs loping in the wake of his cigar smoke, but we also don't
    have his patients suing us for urethral surgery mishaps,

and we can hear the jazz from the Bose speakers of his gazebo on dusky
    Sunday evenings, and we dance on our front stoop,

just hugging really, a long swaying hug, and at least we have
    this cement stoop, right?, and this fenced yard our dog patrols

with full-hearted devotion, as if she's guarding the Taj Mahal,
    and Coltrane on a humid breeze and our hug dances and our glossy

textbook of crazy exes and the medieval tapestry of our jealousies—
    not to mention the pleasure of knowing our children

and our children's children will have ever-increasing latte options
    and even richer neighbors and even crazier, more creative exes.

How Do You Say

Reaching for the phone, I step on the dog's tail,
and she nuzzles my ankle in apologetic
reverence, her perpetual state.

Another friend is calling
for congratulations.
                    Another engagement!

Everyone I know is thinking of falling in love
or falling out of love, either way with both feet on the edge
like the concrete lip of the deep end

and shimmering before them, the cold, drowning water
of adoration or the cold, drowning water of loneliness,
and everyone is referring to the languages of love,

though no one seems to have read the book,
just flipped through the table of contents
at Wal-Mart, but it's enough to know

not all of the languages of love are actual languages,
not French, as you might expect, *mon amour*,
or Italian, *Ti amo, vita mia*, but the language of sweeping

the garage without being asked or necking at the movies
or scooping out the litter box,
so the broom's metronome counts the beat of love

and tongues trace the calligraphy of love
on the cartouche of collarbone, and for my friend
with the pregnant wife, even the kitty litter

spells out love with its alphabet of odors
as he scoops clumps of piss, hissing over his shoulder
at the cats who lattice the shower curtain

and burrow in the mattress, because for cats
the language of love and the language of possession
are lyrics to the same aria, while dogs, those Mozarts,

hum just one uncomplicated bar over and over,
yet we hear the swelling of a symphony.

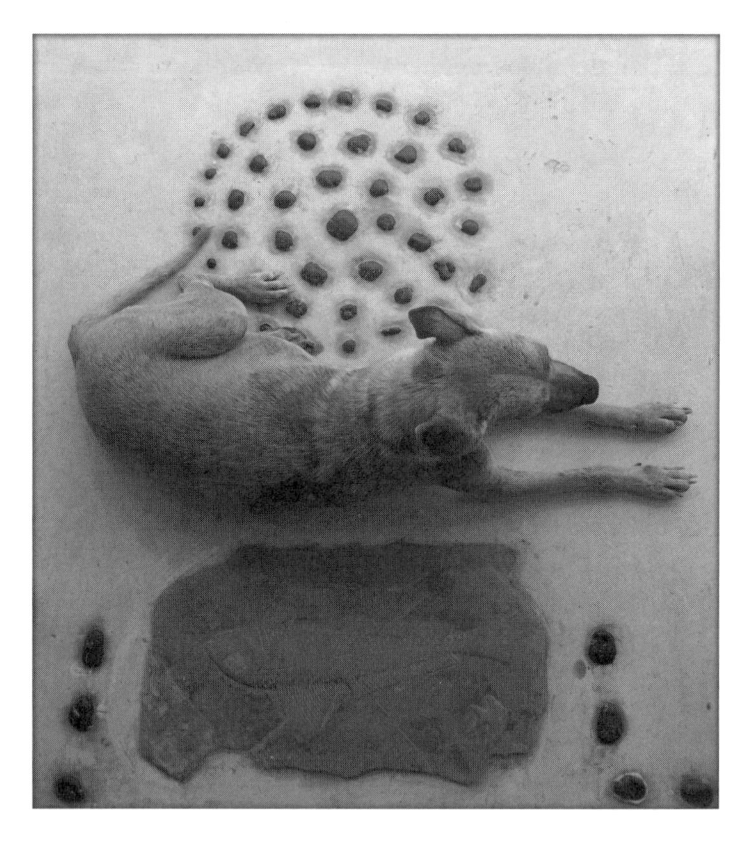

Katherine Minott, *El Sol*, photograph

The Harpsichord Builder's Tale

We are here on the sunporch where our friend is speaking
about the severing, though we already knew the story,
but never from him.
Months later, after he picked them up off the floor,
waited for the helicopter on the front porch, after doctors
sewed them back on and made them work, he leans back in a chair
holding his fingers up to shade his eyes from the sun.

He explains the hand to us. It must be supple
enough to bend, strong enough to stretch out and hold firm.
No more, no less, but proportion is crucial in such binding,
and the doctors, lining up the dangling ligatures in the waning light,
lost measure.
He was alone in the shop, he was making a saw-cut
he had made a thousand times on a harpsichord lid, he knelt
to fumble in the sawdust—could barely tell
one splinter from another—ran down the hall for ice.

We face him in the setting sun, his voice is low, he speaks
only the newest part of the tale, not his journeys under the mountain
where they pulled him through each surgery
helpless against jackals.
His middle finger is thick, and permanently crooked, making it easy
to drop over the reins for riding their black horse (he mimes).
When he puts out his hand towards the new saw-blade ugly birds leer down,
stubble rasps the air, hot pitch flares in his old wound
where the final artery withdrew like a snake
fleeing winter shadows.

Today I notice for the first time the porch floor is gray,
the October sun warms it but pallidly.
After his voice goes still, our fingers tighten
around our slender goblets of Prosecco, the four of us
raise our glasses and pull together
all the strings of all the polished instruments
throughout the house, pull the house,
its chords drawing, being drawn, taut—ringing.

SEMI-FINALIST

DWAINE SPIEKER

Corpus Christi Sunday Afternoon

The slow shadow of a lone cloud
tablecloths the local cemetery,
and on its cotton the dead spread out
their parish picnic, a moveable feast.

Baskets of bread, decanters of wine,
block after block of good cheese.
Adults laugh and dance to accordions
as children play tag in the breeze.

Then the cloud slips off to the east,
taking all but the dead's hospitality.
In sunlight again, you remember the scene,
the way the dead smiled and were waving.

Finalist
Earl Reineman

How to Peel an Apple, 1967

One continuous spiral, of course, unbroken, thin-skinned,
a coiled spring—the way your mother taught you, standing
next to her at the kitchen sink, eleven years old, news of

war casualties coming from the radio perched on top
of the refrigerator, her sharpest knife weighted in your hand,

her seriousness as weighted as if she were teaching you yet
another survival skill—like holding doors open for women,
or helping them with their chair at the dinner table—as she

handed you one apple after another until you mastered the art.
Then, just days later, an early-autumn evening, sitting on the

front porch with Becky Scott from four doors up the street as
she tells of her oldest brother's recent send-off to boot camp—
their home filled for the occasion—aunts and uncles, cousins,

grandparents—the food—each aunt's best potluck dish—
kitchen counters filled with steaming bowls of potatoes, green

beans with bacon cooked slowly for hours, platters of sliced ham
and beef, yeast rolls risen since dawn, butter melting on ears of
corn, apple pies waiting their turn. And Becky's laughter as she

talks of her family's gathering, as darkness begins to settle—
the muffled voice of the radio through the screen door—as you

peel an apple for her—showing off your skill—her ponytail pulled
over her shoulder—her hair a golden tracery of lazy summer sun
and chlorine—her thin, bare arms growing chilled in the dusk as she

folds them tightly across her chest to warm herself, her
summer-tan skin reflecting the yellow glow of the porch light—

her skin, perhaps, as soft and smooth as you might imagine—
the red peel coiling toward your feet—her comfortable,
lingering presence like something imagined, and unimaginable.

Christopher Woods, photograph

Legal Limit, 1968

Myself and two other twelve-year-old boys
from South Hickory Street
gathered like cats whenever the one-armed Mr. Atwell
returned home with his legal limit: six glistening-green
large-mouth bass, fifteen inches or more,
alive and breathing in a five-gallon bucket
of murky lake water.
We had a routine: dump the bucket on the driveway,
let the fish thrash about for a moment, choose
a couple for ourselves, then stand, single-file,
a fish in each hand—holding them by their open mouths—
tail fins dragging—and await our turn at the front of the line,
silently wondering how a one-armed man
could fish so well.

Mr. Atwell—his razor-sharp knife in his only hand
and a Lucky Strike between his lips,
the brim of his fishing hat hiding his eyes—half a dozen lures
hanging on the side like Christmas ornaments.
With a rusted socket wrench and a quick blow to the head
he stunned each fish. One-handed, he cut perfect, thin fillets
while we held the fish tightly in place
against the hard surface of the driveway, the blade
moving precisely—nothing lost or wasted—
white flesh peeling easily from the ribs
as if he could feel every tiny, delicate bone
through the steel blade, up the wooden handle,
and into his hand.

The driveway was smeared with fish blood. Under his breath
Mr. Atwell cursed the enemy soldier who had blown off
his arm in the Korean War. He cursed politicians.
"Learn to fish, boys," he said, loudly enough
to be heard next door.
"A man can survive if he knows how to fish."
He had told us Canada was the place to go—
had told us repeatedly about the fishing up in Canada—

mountain lakes so clear you could see twenty feet to the bottom,
northern pike with teeth like knives,
walleye as long as a man's arm.

With the point of his knife he picked up the slices of meat—
one at a time—stacked them on our outstretched palms
to carry home to our mothers.
I thought of the Nativity play at church,
and the Wise Men, bearing gifts.
Walking home, I thought of politicians—
our dead President Kennedy, who never wore a hat,
who my mother had said was too handsome to wear a hat,
who my father blamed for getting us deep into a new war.
And I thought of our balding President Johnson, talking
on the television about the need
to send more troops.

That evening, after supper, before dark,
I went outdoors
with my rod and reel to practice casting,
pretending to drop the lure with deadly accuracy,
tight against an imaginary sunken log
where the imaginary fish
would be hiding, waiting to strike the lure.
That night I dreamed of a one-armed man in a boat,
on a mountain lake,
somehow—as if he had two good arms—
reeling in fish after fish,
keeping the ones that were big enough to be legal,
releasing the small ones back
into the crystal-clear water.

The Apple

When I was ten or twelve
and all the apples we were going to eat
that winter had been picked
leaving what was left to the frost

my brother bobbed for apples
the water clear enough
to show the stars the moon half-eaten
on the bottom of the tub

he'd chased an apple all the way
disturbed the sunken light
it took so long

I grabbed his shoulders
brought him back
an apple snagged between his teeth
a huge clot of blood

his hair wet and hanging
when he caught his breath
it steamed

SEMI-FINALIST

PENELOPE SCAMBLY SCHOTT

Meanwhile the Dog Just Scratches her Ear

On a hot July day in the 1950's, three kids
mark out a square with a garden hose.
They walk the four sides.

Their red Irish setter
sniffs the length of the hose.

The two big girls have real shovels.
The three-year-old brother
wields a yellow-handled trowel.

The ground is stony and full of bottle caps.
The older kids keep digging.
Wet bangs stick to their foreheads.

The baby brother pats at the lawn
with the back of his trowel.
He sucks hard on the yellow handle.

Now the dog steps onto turned dirt
and flops down where the pool will be.

Move, screams the baby, waving his trowel.
The water of the pool will be so blue
the child is scared the dog might drown.

I want to pretend that I've swum in that pool
for sixty years. The water is clear and blue
and the baby brother is fictional.

Or not. Ghost of my lost uncle,
my mother's younger brother, boy who died
in the Pacific in the middle of World War II.

The dog I have now is a white dog.
When the sky is deep, I think she smells him.

I met him once in his tall dress whites.
I was two. Then he became my mother's grief
flooding my childhood. But how to explain

why my uncle keeps sneaking into my poems?
For all my life he's shadowed me. Please stop.
Even if you had lived, you'd be dead by now.

Christopher Woods, photograph

Our Dog Lily

We call her *Madame Pre-rinse*
because she licks plates.
Dog of gourmet tastes, she's fond
of expensive balsamic vinegar,
and once, just once,
we treated her to octopus. Yes,
that was a hit. And I could go on
with small semi-witty remarks
about the dog or how these hills
are greening like felt
on a billiard table but with hills
too lumpy for billiards
and while you wait for the dog
to trot back into the poem
you are beginning to daydream
about something else,
like the octopus you ate in Spain
or a call you're waiting for
or why I titled this Our Dog Lily
and then dumped her.

Please don't feel bad wandering.
It's completely okay.
In fact, I want you to think about
whatever you think about
when you're not thinking about
something else.
What is that for you? Is it sex?
Sex might be nice.
I don't think about sex nearly
enough these days.
I think about chores unfinished
or chores unstarted.
I think about who has cancer.
Sometimes my eyes itch
and I note everything blooming
too early this spring

and say, *global climate change*
or *wow, those magnolias*
and tomorrow the fallen petals
like a storm of pink snow
will frost the unmown lawn.

Here I could jump back to our dog
who, as you well know,
is really named *Lily,* not *Pre-rinse,*
and discuss recipes
for keeping octopus tender,
or instead I could ask you
where your mind has traveled

since you last paid attention
to my disconnected mumblings
and you may have been
someplace amazing or secret
or maybe just wishing for
a glass of decent red wine
and I could uncork it
and pour two generous glasses
so we could sit here
together with or without the dog
and raise our glasses
and clink them just so and smile
and say honestly
whatever we've been unwilling
to speak out loud
like maybe *Is this really poetry*
or *Please caress my hair.*

SEMI-FINALIST

ARNE WEINGART

The Poet Decides to Stop Writing

for Mark Strand

We could have guessed where you were headed,
I suppose, even from your early work, with its

focus on the edge of the page, the comforting
distance between people and other people, things

and other things. But even liminality, an entire
lifetime of it, has limits. It would take someone

as determined and crafty as you to figure out
how to start unsaying, in that consistent, understated

style, what you've already said. Perhaps you
started not writing too late to undo what you wanted

undone. Or was it mainly your intention to
slowly start the planet rotating in the opposite direction

on its same and only axis? We are taught early on,
if we happened to have been paying attention,

that in the world of real numbers, every integer
has its real and necessary negative. There are

alternative universes, populated only by
mathematical necessity, made plausible by what

we have discovered we may not know. This is where
all the unwritten poems go, traveling out from here,

one by one, converging with what you always
suspected, although unseen, we just might need.

THE NIMROD LITERARY AWARDS
The Katherine Anne Porter Prize for Fiction

HONORABLE MENTION

STEPHANIE CARPENTER

The Sweeper

There's no such thing as . . . "

"*What?*" And I'm awake, the dream is gone. I lie still, straining after details. What was going on, what would I have understood if I hadn't woken up when I did? But I remember only a man's calm voice. I push my sleep mask up my forehead. Still dark. Why do I always wake up too soon?

"—does not exist," the same voice says, firmly.

"What?" I sit up quickly, reaching for my lamp. But I can tell already that the man is not in the apartment or in my head. His voice came from the street. I crawl to the edge of my bed and peer through the blinds.

"There is no such thing as—." A vehicle is turning onto the street, a big, white, blunt-nosed truck. A street sweeper. Its headlights play off the tightly packed brownstones. Speakers are mounted to the top corners of its cab. "—does not exist," it announces again. The missing word is at the same frequency as the truck's spinning brushes.

I shove my window open to hear better. Up and down the street, people are leaning out like me. A few hands extend cellphones over the sidewalk. By the time I find mine, the truck has reached the end of the block. Only then can I hear my neighbors, shouting across our Brooklyn street like it's 1935.

"What the fuck was that?"

"*What* did it say?"

"There's no such thing as humans."

"'Demons'—'demons'!"

"It didn't say shit. Somebody's just messing with you."

"Fuck Brooklyn."

The recording comes again, less robust, playing back through somebody's phone. "There's no such thing as ____," it says. A blank where meaning should be.

"That's some PoMo bullshit right there," yells my downstairs neighbor. He's a first-year in the English Ph.D. program at CUNY.

I feel his window slam shut, directly below mine. Then there's a click, an eruption of tinny sound. Not the truck coming back, but my alarm going off.

* * *

On the subway, at work, everyone is talking about the sweepers. Everybody heard them—those of us in Brooklyn, Queens, the Bronx, Manhattan, Staten Island, Jersey City, Newark . . . even the middle managers who come in from Long Island and Connecticut. Like summer ice cream trucks, street sweepers seem to have canvassed the greater metropolitan area, all playing the same spotty recording.

I work for a standardized test preparation company. We write fake standardized tests; we compose reading comprehension passages and fill-in-the-blank sentences for a living. But though we all seem to have heard the same thing, there is no consensus about what that voice said. We cluster nervously in the centers of our pods—four-person cubicles, ostensible "creative spaces" in which we normally sit oriented to the corners. We've gone through endless K-cups and even more theories by the time the PA system gives its long beep.

"Management is aware of the incident many of you experienced this morning," says a man's nasal voice—not *the* voice. "At this time, there will be no disruption of ordinary business. Our clients are relying on us to help them outsmart the test-makers. Are we going to let them down because of some prankster?"

"Go team!" urges the voice on the PA, and some of us answer in kind. But the announcement only prompts us to work individually. All day I look busy, listing words that might fit the sweeper's blank space. Two syllables—I think. Maybe a terminal -n sound. *Heaven, semen, hoping, dreaming. Women, passion, children*. I am a writer, not just of standardized tests but of fiction (*fiction*?). I moved to New York ten months ago, after finishing my M.F.A.; I moved to New York along with two-thirds of my classmates and who knows how many others, from how many other writing programs. Since then everything I've written has been like this list: it doesn't feel right.

"I heard 'U.N.,'" swears my podmate, Lara. The daughter of U.S. diplomats, she witnessed some bad stuff during her childhood deployments. Now she chairs the office's emergency preparedness squad. All day she wears her orange vest, her supply room keys on a lanyard around her neck. "Or maybe it was 'Yemen,'" she says. So far there's nothing in the news. "Figures," Lara says. "Stay ready."

We had to evacuate the office once before during my tenure, that time because of a blackout. The lot of us milled about Bryant Park for twenty minutes with dozens of other displaced office workers. Then Lara passed out our water rations and we began walking home.

Today we wait for some other catastrophe.

But nothing happens. I clock out after doing even less work than usual, put in my time at the gym, and pick up dinner on the way home. I say hi to my roommate, the cousin of a high school friend, before she heads off to her boyfriend's for the night. Everything is as usual.

And so it continues.

Every morning I wake up just before my alarm to the same calmly delivered, unintelligible message. "____ does not exist. There is no such thing as ____." The sweeper truck moves down my block every day at the same deliberate pace. Its big windows are tinted black. Once I see some Italian guys trailing the thing, a couple of older men in nice suits who hang out at the social club up the block. My nicknames for them are Face and Knuckles and if they are not the Mafioso who are still said to run my neighborhood, then I don't know who are. They keep their distance from the sweeper, watching. Is it doing their work? Or is this a move from Providence? Another morning, the hipsters across the way come surging out of their garden apartment, all three with Go-Pros strapped to their heads. They swing onto the sweeper's running boards and tug at its door handles. But of course they don't manage to get inside. The implacable vehicle keeps moving and they cling to it beyond my line of sight.

In time, a few intrepid bloggers claim to have followed these things to their home bases. On the margins of every borough, every neighborhood, are warehouses, utility sheds—blank-faced buildings holding out against gentrification. The sweepers are reported to retreat into these. But the photos I've seen on Instagram or in the *Post* are inconclusive: just the tail-ends of big machinery, pulling into garages. Who knows whether these are clues—and if they are, to what? The owners of these alleged buildings have not been found. The phone numbers displayed on the sides of such buildings, features of permanent "for rent" signs, are inevitably disconnected, or have been reassigned. One evening my own phone rings. "What does it mean?" screams a woman on the other end. "I know you know!" What can I tell her but "wrong number"—what the ringleaders themselves would probably say, if someone managed to get hold of them. Within a week PSAs appear on the subway, reminding us that 911 is for emergencies only.

All the while I build my collection of words, expanding the list to include words of three syllables. *Washington, abortion, perfection, depression*. I'm no longer even sure about that –n. An aural trick, an aura around the spot where a word should be. I keep a legal pad next to my keyboard; I take notes during lulls in my live-chat test-support shifts. Never before have I been quite this regular in my writing practice—and what does that mean?

"Nice words," my co-worker Alexandro tells me, two weeks into the announcements. He's an affable half-Greek kid on the tech support team; the office celebrated his 23rd birthday with drinks last month at a cheesy Irish pub. Nothing exactly happened between us that night: a lot of joking; some arm- and knee-touching; a kiss on the cheek when my train came first. Since that night he's come by my pod more frequently. Especially, as now, when my podmates are at lunch.

"Revolution," he reads. He leans against my side-desk. "Education, masturbation, communication. All nice words."

"But not *le mot juste*," I say, hoping that like me he doesn't actually speak French. I know this phrase as the title of a course offered in my M.F.A. program. I should have taken that course. "Sometimes I feel like I'm almost there . . . on the brink of figuring it out." I roll my chair away from the monitor's unflattering glow. I'm six years older than he is, already deeply invested in eye creams.

"I think about it in the shower," he tells me. Propped on the side-desk, he push-pulls the base of my chair with his feet. "That's where I go after the truck passes my place. Straight to the shower."

I picture his lanky body, wet. "Tell me more about that part of your process."

"There's some soap, some steam, a lot of rubbing." His feet work my chair slowly.

"And has this yielded any results?"

"Well—those are personal." He stands and drums his long fingers on my legal pad. "We should work on this together."

"Your shower or mine?"

"Definitely yours." He holds my gaze for a moment, shrugs. "But I'm not just a sex object, you know. I've been making recordings, analyzing these messages."

"I'd thought of that, too—that with the right equipment you might be able to hear something."

He shakes his head. "That's not really the result I'm getting. I'd like to show you my data."

"Sure you would."

"Well, I've already seen yours." He biffs my list again. "Are you free later?"

We agree that I will go to his place, after our shifts. I will bring my words, my expertise at word games; I will bring my vocabulary.

"I'll come by for you at five-thirty," he says. Then he drags my roller chair to the middle of the pod and spins me like I'm on a merry-go-round, hand-over-hand. "The spin-off," we call this form of office torture or flirtation, and I fill with heat as I scootch dizzily back to my keyboard. *He's too young,* I tell myself, *he's goofy-looking. He's not a writer.* I slept exclusively with other writers in graduate school and during my first months in New York—men (boys really) who were brilliant, ambitious, unreachable. Here in the city they freelance or edit magazines. They live on nothing and know everyone. I spend 45 hours a week writing practice tests; I can't keep up with them anymore. Seeing such boys at readings or parties or even on the street always leaves me with a heightened awareness of my own tangentiality. I look for myself in their stories, find nothing.

There's no such thing as ____, I repeat to myself at 5:30, as I pack up my things. That sentence is my current project and tonight I am doing research toward it. I hold this in mind as Alexandro and I ride the elevator and walk to his car, a battered station wagon stashed at a broken meter. Caught up in his programming, he'd missed his train that morning and driven in from Yonkers. I seldom take cabs in the city and have never ridden through it like this, in the front seat of a regular car. We listen to The Clash on cassette tape and speed up FDR more nimbly than I'd imagined possible. "It doesn't bother you," he asks me, feigning a thick accent, "my Greek driving?" "It doesn't bother you?" he asks again, when he reveals his rented room—one dim chamber in a sub-basement, with a shared kitchen and bath. The last writer I slept with lived in NoHo, in a flat purchased and expensively decorated by his mother. He considered it bourgeois to own books. Alexandro might, too, from the look of things. I tell him the apartment doesn't bother me.

"Have a seat." He offers the only seat, a frayed desk chair. When I sit it rolls freely on the bare linoleum and he catches it by the arms.

"No spin-off." I wrap my ankle around his calf—to stop him, to start something else. But he lets go.

"I'll get us drinks." His dark hair nearly touches the room's dropped ceiling. "Don't open the door to strangers."

Does this imply that we are something else? I roll to Alexandro's desk, pass the mouse across its pad. The two huge monitors wake. Hubble photographs fill the screens, bright and fathomless. *There is no such thing as—*

"For you." He's drinking a High Life but hands me a can of Guinness—what I ordered on his birthday. He takes up the wireless keyboard and sits just behind me, on the edge of his neatly-made bed. Everything about the room is tidy, albeit cramped and dingy. Plastic sets of drawers hold his clothes along the room's margins. A stack of USED textbooks serves as a bedside table. (Books, after all). A poster of *The Scream*; a poster of *The Kiss*.

"It's like a dorm room," I say. "I guess that makes sense."

"Four-fifty a month," he says. "Utilities included."

That's less than half my Brooklyn rent. But from the room next door comes a man's anguished grunting, the clang of metal on metal.

"Weights," Alexandro says, typing. "Every night."

"Or a minotaur," I suggest.

"Ah." He feigns the accent again. "You know my people's culture?"

I shrug. "How do you say—" I point to the door.

"Pórta." He gives me the Greek words for desk, chair, floor, ceiling, hand. We are here to share words, after all. I point to the window, the floor, my foot. I point to *The Scream*. I swivel the desk chair toward him, point to *The Kiss*.

"To filí," he says. "Filí mou."

"Feely moo?" I repeat.

"This means 'kiss me,'" he says, still in that ridiculous voice. "Filí mou."

The sounds are unsensual, silly even, but his long torso tapers trimly to his waist—and I think of a filmstrip from middle school that illustrated the Pythagorean theorem by tracing triangles on cartoon Greek bodies. I have a square Scandinavian head; I have an attraction to broad shoulders, national geometries. I draw the keyboard from his lap and lean toward him and he tugs my chair closer, leaning toward me. His mouth tastes like cheap beer. His mouth tastes like college, this room feels like college, and it is like going back in time when he pulls me from the desk chair and onto his thighs. "Should I get a—" he asks, when our clothes are off. "Yes," I say, and he dives from the bed toward those plastic drawers, searching until he finds a condom. It is like college sex, enthusiastic and a little clumsy, except for the way he watches me with those big eyes—and for the reasons that I close mine.

"Would you have come home with me that night at McGillicuddy's?" he asks, kissing me afterward.

"No." I had gone home after his birthday celebration and written in my notebook—pages barely decipherable the next morning. The final maudlin lines sometimes run through my head: "as if lodged between lives and craving / you." Lines with no definite object—but I am no poet.

"I'm glad you did tonight. But I don't want you to think I brought you back here just to fool around."

There are no pillows on his bed and his Pythagorean chest is hard and hairy beneath my cheek. "Why not?" *What else is possible between us?* I am already thinking. *What am I doing here?*

"Come here." He loops his long arms around my waist and pulls me with him to the foot of the bed. "Look at these."

The left monitor fills with jagged strata: peaks and valleys, drawn in electric colors. "Sound waves?"

"This is a week's worth of messages." He scrolls through, pointing out little differences from day to day, modulations in the sweeper's unvarying message. The differences elude my ear, even when he plays the audio back slowly. "Why are they re-recording this, every time?"

"Maybe someone is actually speaking—it's not a recording after all?"

"No." He shows me the data from a single day: the pattern of waves repeats exactly. "It's just a recorded loop. But you see how each day differs from the days before and after it. A different recording, every day."

"Even the blank is different." Because on the screen I can see it for a blank. Not a murmur, but a gap in the message, silence except for the static of the speakers. These blanks vary in duration.

"So different things must fit in those blanks." He looks at me in the computer light, and though he is much younger than me his deep-set eyes give an impression of wisdom.

"*If* the blanks have meaning at all," I say, remembering the assessment of my neighbor: *PoMo bullshit*. "These variations might just be part of the project—tempting people like you and me to look for meaning where there isn't any."

"Maybe." He kisses me. "But I don't think so. Let's say that we accessed the database of an online dictionary, one with audio pronunciations. And we synced these sweeper recordings to the speed of the dictionary-reader."

"Okay," I say. "But it's not as though words have unique durations. There would still be thousands of words that might fit each of these blanks."

"But we would narrow down the possibilities. A really awesome computer program could do that for us." He types quickly and a list of dates and numbers appears on the other monitor.

"Such as yours already has . . ." I trace his long spine with my fingertips, its curve toward the computer. "Am I here to go through all the eligible words?"

"There's no point," he says. "I mean, at first I thought, yes, that would be the next step. But look—" He lunges across his desk, grabs a legal pad like mine. "I wanted someone else to see . . . by the time I finished writing the program, I had six days of recordings. And these are the numbers of possible words that my program originally yielded for each day's blank. I backed everything up on paper."

On the page of his legal pad dated May 6th, he's written the durations of the blanks broadcast on May 1st, 2nd, 3rd, 4th, 5th, and 6th, respectively, along with the numbers of possible words for each of those blanks. In black ink, his numbers are vigorous and clear. The next sheet in the notebook is dated May 7th, with data for the dates May 1st-7th. And so on through May 13th, today.

"Now look at how some of the results change. Like this .67 second blank from May 2nd. See how the number of possibilities for that blank dropped by one digit when I ran the program on May 4th, then dropped again on May 10th?"

On the screen I see that the May 2nd tally is now 37,219 instead of 37,221, as he'd originally recorded: 37,219 possible words instead of 37,221. He watches me glancing back and forth.

"And do you see what else is special about those two dates? The blanks for May 4th and May 10th are also .67 seconds long."

"So the same word fits all three blanks?" I rub my eyes, squinting.

"Well yeah, it could, but we can't realistically determine that: too many possibilities. My point is that every time the recorded blank is .67 long, there's one less eligible word."

"One fewer," I say, reflexively. "Possibilities are countable." This is the stuff of standardized tests; this is familiar.

"Okay." He runs his hand across his face, across the bristle of black stubble coming out along his jaw. "But do you see what I'm saying? Words are disappearing from this tally. Every blank of .67 seconds should yield exactly the same number of possible words: 37,221. Why does the count drop by one digit every time—and why is it dropping retroactively?"

"Your program could have an error," I suggest. "And dictionaries are revised periodically."

"Believe me, I've checked my work. There's nothing wrong with the code. And you can't tell me they revise the dictionary every day."

I look at him in the semi-darkness, a stranger. "So what's your hypothesis?"

He gestures at the analytics he's generated. "It's taking away words. The street sweeper."

My skin prickles, as though somebody has walked over my grave. Ridiculous—the suggestion, my reaction. Am I afraid of his theory? Or of a person who would offer this as a valid proposition? I drop back onto the mattress. Big HVAC pipes hang directly over my head. Real pipes, ugly and encroaching. Tangible. I know myself to be too impressed by tangible things. But the theory, the ceiling, the car, the posters, the clanging of metal coming again from next door . . . *what am I doing here?*

"I should go," I tell him. "I work tomorrow, and I'm sure it's going to take a while to get back to Brooklyn."

"Oh." He looks down at me. "I thought you might stay."

"I should go. If you can drop me at the train that'd be great."

"Sure." He turns off the monitors, turns back to me. His face is dark. "Do I really sound that crazy?"

"It's not that. It's just . . . I haven't been getting much sleep with these messages and everything, and I think it's best if we slow this down. Think it through."

"Sure." He pulls on his t-shirt. "But what if I'm right?"

What if he *is* right—and I'm just a sour disbeliever, heading home to have my words erased while I sleep? Worst-case scenario: a word a day isn't much. There are so many words that mean practically the same things, so many words we'd never miss. James Joyce used over 30,000 different words in *Ulysses*. More words, possibly, than I'll use in my lifetime. The vocabulary of Agatha Christie's novels shrank by thirty percent in the last twenty years of her life. Computer analysis shows this—I heard about it on NPR. But even without that thirty percent, she could write books. Diminished books, maybe; I can't say. I have never read any of her work (just as I've never read *Ulysses*). I've only heard her story, a story told by computers. Computers can show us what we don't feel—or don't want to: the contracting of our abilities. And I can't seem to write anymore . . . though that started months before the sweeper came.

"This isn't much data," I tell him. "This is correlation, not causation." A logical fallacy that I am paid to practice, in writing wrong answers for fake standardized tests.

"Don't you hate that feeling," he says, looking at me with his owlish eyes, "when you're trying to remember a word and you can't? Such a relief when it comes to you. But what if it didn't?"

"You said you wanted me to bring my list. If a word is missing, how could I have it?"

"You don't," he says. "None of us does."

"Oh, come on." I shake my head, angry now. "What if something I wrote down two weeks ago just got swept yesterday? It's still in my notepad, right? Or was I compelled by some *force* to erase it?"

"The brain fills in all kinds of gaps, all the time. You must know that." He sounds exhausted—or disappointed—looking away from me into a dark corner of the room. "If one of the swept words is in your notes, we just can't see it anymore. That's what *I* think."

"Okay." I sit up next to him. "Say I believe you. How is it possible? You think it's some kind of hypnosis, the sweeping? A government conspiracy?"

He wakes up the monitors again. "That's the part I don't understand. I see the effects, not the cause."

"And not the reason."

"There are a million reasons to take away people's words," he says. "And if we don't notice it's happening?"

I shiver again and he puts an arm around me. That searching feeling, the trace of something not quite remembered . . . it's been the hallmark of my existence, these past two weeks. A feeling I wake up to that never quite goes away. I kiss him and we move together again, more solemnly this time. We are searching, he and I, only pretending to be beyond words.

After sex I stare again at that ugly ceiling. "For argument's sake—let's say this is happening. How could we prove it?"

"Besides this?" He gestures toward his data. "Numbers seem like the best proof."

I rub my eyes. "If you can't demonstrate that something is missing, the numbers don't mean anything."

"Well . . ." He props himself on an elbow, strokes my arm. "I have another idea, too. Say I—*we*—went away somewhere—like up into Canada. If we found a place where these messages couldn't reach us, when we came back, we'd be able to see what was missing."

It sounds like a romantic crusade: a writer and a programmer, saving the English language. "Do you know how to camp?"

"Camping is just sleeping outside."

I try to imagine the two of us alone in a tent. Is he a hero or a lunatic? How will we pass the time? "We should bring a lot of books . . . all kinds of books, so that we have as many words as possible shored up for when we come back."

"Or we could just take a bunch of vocab flashcards."

Our company's proprietary cards are filled with words like "mendacious," "risible," "noisome." Are these the words we should be safeguarding? "Refulgent," I say to him. "Nonplussed."

"You're right," he tells me. "I minored in Poly Sci—we should take those books."

I fill a duffel bag with USED copies of Tocqueville and Studs Terkel while he sets up a recording device in the window. It will upload the sweeper announcements directly to his cloud storage, he tells me: the data will keep coming, the blanks will be recorded and archived, even after we're gone. We pack his station wagon with his big desktop computer, a mildewed tent, and all the food from the shared kitchen, and we drive to Brooklyn to get my things: clothes, skin care products, my unread copy of *Ulysses*. We don't look at the clock as carefully as we might, between these errands and that shower we'd teased each other about. He translates the label of my fancy Greek shower gel: *uplifting, clean and fresh*. I confess that I thought of him when I bought it. Thus we are just fastening our seatbelts again when we hear the sweeper coming. "____ does not exist," it announces, as it does every morning. The man's voice is commanding but patient. "There is no such thing as ____." Now I know that the gap is powerful, potent. It represents something I don't want to lose. It represents what I've already lost.

"Come on," I urge Alexandro. He fumbles with the key, his long hand seeming to tremble in the faint light. Finally the engine turns over but we are parked in so closely that he will have to inch the car out of the spot.

The city itself is a machine that takes things away—I have learned this much in ten months. It's taken away the energy I had when I moved here, my faith that I am a writer, a faith that was never about having a degree, but grew during the experience of getting it. Those years of school were like being in a big tent with books, in the middle of nowhere, unsure whether the other campers were heroes or lunatics. I could be in the tent again, if Alexandro's car would just move, if the two of us could believe in his idea long enough to reach the border, show our passports, find a pine forest without bugs or drunks or other, brighter tents luring us apart. *Stay with me,* I want to say—words that won't come, and not because I've lost them.

The sweeper must be stalled; it isn't advancing. "Look," Alexandro says, shoving open the car's sunroof. I rise through it, swaying as he edges his way out of the spot. Down the street I can see a line of people across the sweeper's path: the Mafioso, the hipsters, the Eritrean family that runs the laundromat.

"People are blocking it," I tell him. "Should we help?"

He puts his hand on my thigh, pulling me down into the passenger seat. "What do you want to do?" The car's front bumper is clear of the parking spot. "Do you want to go with me and figure this thing out—or do you want to stay here and be part of whatever's going on?" He looks stern in the half-light—as well as young, goofy, unlettered.

I think of the mildewed tent staked in the woods, of the two of us sweaty and unshowered, having sex and eating granola bars, isolated from everyone else. How long can we call in sick before we lose our jobs—and how obvious will it be to our coworkers that we're calling in sick *together*? How will I explain myself to my roommate; will she even notice I'm gone? And when we come back, what then? If no one has stopped these sweepers so far, what difference could the two of us make?

I think also of my legal pad, out in the woods, filling up not just with words but with work—as it did when I lived in that other, institutionalized tent in the woods. We could spend our afternoons reading, Alexandro and I; we could finally get to things too long or complicated to read on the subway. And it wouldn't just be self-indulgent, our life in the woods. When we came back . . . when we came back, we would have to find a means of broadcasting our words. We would have to re-educate New York: Thoreau meets sci-fi. No one in the writing world would have noticed my disappearance; how, then, could I expect them to take notice of my reappearance? Did I have it in me to stand with Alexandro and try to speak—knowing that we wouldn't be heard? And that's presuming that Alexandro's program will show us the truth, and that we will return with a truth to speak.

"Are you coming or not?" Alexandro asks. He's fixated on the rearview mirror.

The car promises me one thing and the city another, and if the city has withheld its promise from me so far, on this morning it seems to invite me into it, through the linked arms of my neighbors. I kiss Alexandro and then . . . I want to believe that I do the right thing. As I switch this story now from present tense, with its conceit that all of this is still unfolding, still malleable, into past tense, the only true tense, I would like to believe that I took a risk, made a brave choice that morning when I got out of the car and joined the protest. What I can tell you is that my neighbors' names are John Sciboni and Lester Minkins, and they are not mobsters but a gay couple, both real estate developers. For a week or so I stood with them every morning, my arms linked with theirs, letting the sweeper nudge me down the street. For a month or so after that the hipsters and I chatted on the subway, comparing the fading sweeper bruises on our hips and making abstract plans to see a show or get a drink sometime. Once I even gave a reading with some of my M.F.A. classmates—work inspired by the sweeper. We wrote flash fiction about the sweeper as a social experiment, a government conspiracy, a projection of the collective unconscious. I wrote a prose poem for the occasion, using only words that could be fashioned from the letters of Alexandro's full name, Alexandro Stephen Constanopolous.

She scans her phone: no calls, no texts. A screen as clean as a street. No note under her door; no last letter. No shouts or harsh sex or other upsets—only a deep pull north. He's an axe; she's a spoon. Salt-laden, she spoon-races to the sea. The scoured streets contract and trap. But the sea, that surplus—the sea sounds, ceaselessly. The truth's a red coal that sears her. The sea drenches her, but doesn't put her out. Now she's a corroded spoon, anchored to shore. He showed her a truth that a spoon can't shout: no throat, no sound. She echoes as a shell, alone.

At 108 words, "A Spoon Can't Shout" was the longest piece I'd finished since grad school—and I broke my constraint only three times. No one else was paying attention; no one else could have known what well those letters were drawn from.

In time we all got used to the sweeper's message; it became meaningless. A street evangelist might preach about it; a homeless person rant about it. And sometimes even now when I wake up in the morning I can almost hear the word not said by that calm, emphatic voice. Other mornings I sleep right through it. At work, Alexandro was soon replaced, though I don't know whether news of his termination reached him. Before long there was another gangly kid in his early 20s, occupying Alexandro's place in tech support pod, solving our customers' problems with the test-taking software. "Send word," I'd said to him that morning, after I kissed him and before I got out of his car. A stupid thing to ask for—the thing most likely to vanish before it reached me. I'd thought I was being playful. Now I remind myself that he could have stood with me that morning, tried one thing before he tried the other. I wish he would have; I think I might have driven away with him after the neighbors unlinked their arms. I think I might have been convinced after that one additional test. Call it a stress test: how much pressure can a human barricade withstand? How much of the problem did we even grasp? But by the time the sweeper nosed through our arms that morning, Alexandro was gone.

Eleanor Leonne Bennett, photograph

Comparative Onomastics

I asked what her name meant, and she supplied
a sestina of answers, Kurdish and Arabic:

1. "*Easy.*" A pre-emptive punchline, flirting
quietly with the ironic. "*For example, 'It was easy
to memorize this poem.'*" Not hard, I guess
that's true—yielding when appropriate. A little bit
tao, the responsive smoothness of a river stone.

2. "*A raindrop.*" Understated but
singular. Pure. Solace to a desiccated
man. Willfully unremarkable
but undiluted even in an ocean.
Gracious such small hands.

3. "*The sound of waterfalls.*" The plural
here is vital. The first fall never sounds
quite like the next. The polyglot's fluent
murmur of call and descending echo.

4. "*A river in heaven.*" Galactic
throughout its length, headwaters
to mouth. Silvered and swift-
footed and perilous. Drink deep or at
least grab an oar and set to.

5. "*A plural of the name that means a beautiful young lady.*"
More than one, yes. But a *pluralis maiestatis*?
Or because she is more beautiful than any single
woman has a right to be? A muse, garden-
dwelling, tangible, blessing, young, so young.

6. "*A white rose on a high mountain.*"
Too conventional to be quite right. Let's make it
a primrose: smaller, less obvious. And purple,
almost black. Unruffled in the thin air,
sensuous, luminous beneath the cool rain.

Song, ease her name in raindrops through the sound
of waterfalls and along the heavenly river to the beautiful
young lady who blooms on a high mountain.

Katherine Minott, *Morning Prayer,* photograph

SECOND PRIZE
LEILA CHATTI

Momon Eats an Apple in Summer

She keeps each sliver
to herself. Her fingers draw

the blade through the flesh
up to the bed of her thumb,

and stop
and there is no blood—she knows

not the day or my name, but this,
how to slice through

safely, understands
still the realm of pain.

Her face, old fruit
left in a bowl

washed with sun.
Her name is the echo

of apple—*tafahah, Téfida*.
She sings it

like a chant,
calls through each room of the house

Téfida, Téfida, Téfida
searching for herself.

She pares the fruit
down to its tough spine,

the apple dismantled, the skin
stripped into green half-moons

placed in a shallow dish, their bellies
the color of teeth, of bone.

Preparing Iftar with My Father

God's word calling through the stereo
in a man's voice. My father murmurs

in chorus, closes his eyes into two
lash-lined crescents as he washes the carrots

and reaches for the knife.
I peel the potato and mine

out its muddy eyes. Steam hovers
beneath kitchen cupboards, trapped and turning

to tiny beads. Water roils
at the bottom of the pot, each escaped bubble

flashing silver before breaking.
My father slides in

the sliced vegetables, salt, a pinch
of pepper the color

that has appeared like metal
slivers in his beard. He is fifty now.

All his life he has known hunger:
bowl of his stomach, belly round as a moon.

Added up, he has gone
three years without food.

He prepares patiently
a pan of oil,

chops parsley for the *brik*.
I fetch the carton of shivering eggs

and grab the *malsouka* sheets.
My father hums; the sound fills him.

Late sun seeps in, spreads
gold as yolk,

as night pulls slowly over us
her heaven-lined cloak.

Christopher Woods, *Late September Dawn,* photograph

A Religious Education

I learned to be flexible—those positions boys like—
from five daily contortions

into the bathroom sink. I can reach my foot up
and rest it in the basin, can cock my head

to drink from the stream between metal
lip and porcelain bowl.

Watching the men bending
down to pray in their rows, I learned

the intricate curvatures
of the other body: cavern of the throat

calling to God, that O of the mouth.
Each rack of shoulders, each sloped back and mound

of ass, I liked to watch them kneel
and fall forward, kneel and fall forward,

lips hovered just above the rug. There,
I learned my body too.

Sundays,
my hips practiced their shifting sway,

slow crossing through the men's side to join
my kind. And each year I learned better

to hunger, my stomach a fist, those long days
of fasting, holy month of appetite, ritual of

anticipation. I eyed the men passing,
a starved woman, that ache in me

pulsing, its red mouth hissing *wait, wait, soon.*

Tunis Nocturne

Moon, pearly fishbone

lodged in the night's black throat.
Through the dark, a cat

yowls, noses trash
for scraps. I pass

buildings stacked
like towers of salt, and ahead

a minaret looms, its silent needle
pointed towards God.

It could coax a song from
the vinyl of heaven

and the song would sound
like weeping. All prayer is

a pleading. Men murmur
in cafés and exhale slowly,

shisha smoke rising
in silver curls. The coals turn

to ash, crumble in their dish, disintegrate.
I walk out of range of voices and soot.

A window burns down the street,
third story, the solitary light.

Someone always, waiting.

HONORABLE MENTION
BERWYN MOORE

Interferon

Three hours after the needle
stick in one or the other thigh,

alternating each week
to confound the bruising,

I crumple in a frozen field,
my breath curling in crescents.

A magpie cleaves the darkness,
then pecks the side of my head,

accusing me of sleeping.
My bones shake against my will.

My skin no longer fits, stretching
and stinging as I try to climb out

of it, but I can't lift myself high
enough. Field mice gnaw my toes.

The clouds' heavy rasps muffle
my voice, and snow veils my eyes.

I give myself up. Every eyelash,
muscle, nerve, and cell surrendered.

Only one thing will I claim when it
comes at the nadir of this long night—

the scent of almonds or clover,
sometimes tapioca, sneaking in

with the light, sweet molecules
infusing my lungs, nudging me

toward blue linen and clean socks,
my husband's voice calling me back.

Shoshana Kertesz, photograph

What the Wind Said

Psithurism: the sound of wind in the trees

We've all heard it, the scorn of rain
on the roof, the fuss of forgotten sheets
on the line, the *psst psst* of pine needles
slapping the pane. But this time, the wind

barges in, burgling the gloom I've nestled
into, scattering the silence and shuffling
the torn-off calendar days pyramided
on the desk. She breathes my shape

into the shirt hanging on the chair,
then drops it on the floor, sets frames
askew, gilds the room in corn dust
and feathers. Her silky skirts swoosh

by my bed, her snickers and *tsk tsks*
collect in the corners. True to her windy
self, she ruffles and marks everything
as hers, no line taped to the floor

dividing what's mine and what's hers,
all of it sliding beneath a watery blue
wave. My heart thumps *almost, almost*.
I grip the sheets and close my eyes,

ambling from this room to the dream's
snare: a baby tumbling through a chute
from sky to earth, and each time I'm almost
there to catch him, bystanders *tsk, tsking*

their disapproval, the baby whooshing
out to who knows where, and I wake
up to the same old grief hunching over
me, luring me back to limbless sleep.

But now, stirred by the rumple and whirr
of air in motion, the scruffy yowl, the prism
of red and purple quivering on the wall,
I rush to claim him, arms spread wide as wind.

Tinnitus

The brain thickens with noise.
A cricket scritches somewhere

in the house, in February, snow
lacing the windows. A dentist's

drill screeches while I shower.
Someone cracks ice from a tray

in the dark kitchen. An endless
sizzle of fish frying. The caterwaul

of rusted brakes on the empty street.
Perhaps the wind of our quarrel,

trapped in my ear, swirls its harsh
accusations. Maybe the neighbor

dreams of sirens or burglars rattle
the latch. Before I drip rose oil

into my ears or stuff them with salve,
earthworms boiled in goose grease,

let me hold fresh loaves, steaming
from the oven, tight against my head.

Let me imagine silence—the violet
unfurling its petals, a pause, stars

pulsing, dew lifting from the grass.
And if this feverish hood fails

to muffle the bones' quiver, then
let me conjure chimes and chants,

cowbells in a distant field, children
singing *a cappella*, the moon ticking

across the sky, a t-shirt fluttering,
a shovel without its burden of dirt.

Katherine Minott, *Whispers*, photograph

THE NIMROD LITERARY AWARDS
The Pablo Neruda Prize for Poetry

FINALIST
LISA C. KRUEGER

Parallax at Nine a.m.

Can't locate herself. Children are calling again, one to complain about work, one to ask for money. Everything feels immediate and necessary. Unloading the dishwasher, step-by-step. Late summer presses at her, smell of peaches on the counter, gardenias in a vase. Cut grass and early smog, its bleached, burned tingle. Since when is the body slow? Dishes can take forever. *Hurry up,* her mind commands. Loneliness has no season, she decides. Birthing, breast-feeding, solace-keeping only change the weather. She wonders where all the dishes went, turning this way and that. *I am sorry, I am sorry,* she says to the receiver.

Distance

My aunt was the kind of shrink who dropped acid with Timothy Leary to be *at the mind's frontier*. My aunt did not like people-pleasers. At holidays she brought us sugar-dusted nougats in narrow boxes and provoked arguments between my parents. She liked to sit, smoke and watch. Sometimes I felt desperate to make my parents stop. I would say anything for silence. One Thanksgiving my aunt leaned forward through the clouds to ask me: *Is that what you really think?* Her eyes were gray-blue like mine. Sometimes I looked at her and thought I was looking at myself. She liked my little sister better. My aunt was a communist who moved to Rome. The summer I was fourteen we visited her flat above a broken, vast plaza filled with families who stopped talking to watch us. Over drinks her painter-friend said I was his *Botticelli-muse*, when could I pose. My father made us leave. We ate gelato in the plaza and stepped on shards of glass by our car. Someone stole my father's Dictaphone. Maybe my aunt liked rebels. When she died she left all her money and jewelry to my sister who said *I have no need for decorative shit* and gave me the woven box. Inside is a jungle of sweater pins, cameos, fake diamonds and pearls, imitation turquoise-studded chokers and cuffs. Sometimes for therapy I choose a pin or necklace. Sometimes a client pauses to say *Well that is an interesting spider you are wearing* and then my aunt is right there in the room. Once at the very bottom of the box I found a pendant with the double-venus sign. I want to ask my aunt about it. I want to ask her what she learned from LSD. I want to ask her why distance alters perspective, and how she knew I lied.

The Latin of It

Fuchsia petals used to scattershot
center divides of the 5, the 110:
her L.A., her *urbs angelicorum*.

When she was young, every street
had oleander, every kid reached
for the dangerous bloom.

Don't touch, her mother had said.
Don't touch, she told her children.
A neighbor lost the custody battle

then steeped leaves for tea; she didn't
completely die. An oleander memory,
a *nerium memoria.*

Oleander has suffered from *Bacterium*
Xylella Fastidiosa. On her freeways,
soundproof barriers replace skeletons.

She once held the scent
of her babies' skin like a flower,
their voices a *tendri flos*—

Searching

Her nose drips
green pepper,
small mounds of moist
meat round out chin and cheeks.
Mary on meatloaf.

Her son is turning up in odd locations—
on a clean, crumpled sock in England.
In the States, he's seared himself into a stick of fish,
burnt his profile into a wedge of Texas toast.
Somewhere else, her snack-sized son is a Cheeto
curled in prayer.

She wants to lean on Joseph, tell him
this is no way to save the world
but her husband is nowhere to be found.
So Mary gathers up her congealed veil of holy
and seeps into the whorled, wooden door of the
Riddle family trailer.

She is closing in on her boy,
every grain of her being ablaze.

SEMI-FINALIST

WENDY BARKER

The Hollow

of a silver spoon, a palm,
fingers curling a shallow bowl.

To spoonfeed. Applesauce,
oatmeal, cream of wheat, chicken

broth. To enter the cave
of a waiting mouth. The bowl

upturned, emptied of
the little it carries.

The Sterling Platter

is engraved with patterns
of vines and leaves, florid

intricacies hidden when laden with
porcelain cups and saucers, sugar bowl

and creamer, teapot, and white damask
napkins, so you don't notice the design

coils like a labyrinth with
no way in, or out.

Mom's Creamer

holds only a few
drops, just enough

to soften the bite of over-
steeped lapsang souchong

during late afternoon tea,
which she spent in her final

years alone, unless a daughter
happened to visit. The etched

oval on the side carries no
image—a cameo without

a face. The silver lip of
the creamer angles

to a point, sharp little
beak—peck, peck.

The Dragon Bowl

was the one piece I asked
my sister to send when she decided

to sell all Mom's silver, not because
it was sterling because it wasn't, only plate,

but for the sweeping creature, its tail, spikes,
fangs, claws reaching toward a bulbuous sun with

rays that spewed in every direction like the creature
itself spiralling round and round, looping its scaly

body etched and chased across the bowl's width,
this animal whose power for the Chinese lay

in its shedding skin, emerging as a new,
transformed being, able to soar, see

from a great height what has been
and what will come of it.

HONORABLE MENTION
KRISTINA GORCHEVA-NEWBERRY

The Heart of Things

When Leezy phones to inform her that their mother had a heart attack, Carmen is still in bed, on the cusp of sleep, diving in and out of a dream in which she's being led across the ocean by some unknown invisible force. The space around her widens with each step and the only scrap of land has long disappeared from view. She wears loose white vestments with a red cape that flickers in the wind like a bloody tongue. The ringing breaks through her dream in spells; she trips—her robe catching on a stone or a fish, a mossy carapace of a turtle—and falls, sinks through the layers of water and kelp, sea anemones, silt-coated oyster reefs. She attempts to shout, but her mouth fills with algae, her hair strewn with limpets and barnacles, baby starfish. To her dread and utter fascination, she discovers her mermaid tail, emerald green, housing a shoal of tiny creatures under the sharp iridescent scales.

Carmen opens her eyes; the room is dark, the curtains pulled shut. The machine blinks with Leezy's message that Carmen replays a few times before getting up and walking to the bathroom, where she splashes her face with cold water until her skin tingles. She imagines her sister returning home from an apothecary and discovering their mother on the floor, her long hair a lake of quicksilver. Their mother has always insisted that long hair is all women have these days to set them apart; their desire to be independent—pantsuits and briefcases—has taken all the femininity out of them. "Cutting off your hair results in cutting off your beauty together with your wisdom," her mother once said, and Carmen didn't argue because the experience of being raised by a stern, mighty-shouldered woman who possessed the will of all the men Carmen had dated told her not to waste her time or breath—her mother would not change.

Carmen has been living in the States for seventeen years, since 1996. She had come to visit an American she'd met in Red

Square, then got hired by a local dinner theatre and stayed. At the theatre, Carmen first worked as a waitress, but she was tall and shapely, could sing, dance, and speak decent English. The productions were all musicals—*The Wizard of Oz, Oklahoma!, Hello, Dolly!, The Fantasticks*—so six months later, she began acting too, small parts, group scenes. She left the man who'd courted her and moved in with one of the actresses. Life became exactly what Carmen had imagined it to be. She performed, partied, got high, engaged in euphoric tireless sex, swooning in clouds of smoke and fog. She woke up in lounge chairs by pools or on private beaches, half-buried in sand, listening to waves slosh ashore while the sun lit up the world.

Unlike her sister, Carmen has never wanted to marry the Prince of Wales. Nor has she longed for a magical someone to walk into her life and sweep her off her feet. Leezy has always been different. As a child, she was dreamy and sullen, bone thin. No matter how much their mother tried to fatten her up and turn Leezy into a plump, robust woman a man would want to bear his children—"hips," their mother said, "it's all in the hips, the woman's strength and passion"—all her efforts failed. Leezy stayed pale and gangly, nose in a book. At forty-five, Leezy still hasn't married, and Carmen is swept with pity, comparing their childhood pictures to the more recent ones, diligently sent to Carmen by their mother once a year.

There has been a fleet of men in Carmen's life and only one in Leezy's—the guy she dated in her university years. Right after graduation, he left Leezy for her best friend, with whom he did things Leezy refused to do. "What kind of things?" their mother asked. But Leezy wouldn't answer. She shook her head and stuck her tongue out and pretended to gag. Carmen was thirteen then and had a vague idea what her sister was talking about, so she laughed like crazy, spitting crumbs of supper onto her plate. Their mother reached out and slapped her on the cheek, which startled Carmen, but also infuriated her. From that moment on, she felt that the balance had somehow shifted, that their mother would always side with Leezy because she, too, was the abandoned one, the one who needed the most love and care.

They haven't talked for eternity, her sister and she, and Carmen hasn't seen her mother since that last visit, five years ago. Carmen was thirty then, still working at the same theatre, which her mother failed to acknowledge. Real theatre was only in Moscow, as far as she was concerned. And what her daughter did—jumping on stage in tight tops and short ruffled skirts that looked like cheap lingerie—was not acting or even performing. It was vulgar entertainment for a certain kind of clientele who didn't know any better. They quarreled—a lot—about food, movies, books, clothes, which was nothing unusual, but at some point Carmen phoned her sister to tell her that she'd be putting their mother on the first available flight from Miami to Moscow. Leezy didn't answer but hung up.

* * *

On the plane, Carmen sits next to a man whose white, starched shirt and shaved face suggest that he must be an office worker. Carmen guesses him to be forty or a bit older. He has no ring on either hand. As soon as they are offered drinks, the man introduces himself as Josh and asks for a beer, while Carmen prefers cognac.

Josh is American with a Russian ancestor on his mother's side—the reason for his two-week trip. "To dig for roots," he jokes. "You?"

"I have no roots," Carmen says. "Just bloody relatives."

Josh laughs. When she inquires what he does, he's hesitant for a moment, then says, "I'm a doll-maker."

"You mean like Barbies?" she asks, even more puzzled. "Really?"

He shakes his head. "Old dolls, like Pinocchio, Petrushka—theatre puppets. I work for a European company."

"I was born in a theatre," Carmen says, well aware of how odd it sounds.

"Your mother is an actress?"

"No. She used to sell tickets. But she loves theatre more than men." Carmen grins, adding, "She was already in labor and refused to leave the opera. Hence my name." She takes a sip of cognac, then asks, "What does *your* mother do?"

"Don't know. I grew up in an orphanage, been to a few foster homes. I was a mean child, got into fights constantly. No one kept me long."

Carmen doesn't know how to respond to such honesty. When she first came to America, the man she was staying with warned her that "How do you do?" was a rhetorical question; it demanded no answer other than "Fine, thank you." Her actress roommate told Carmen not to elaborate on any personal illnesses or dramas, not to pry into people's private business, even if they were willing to share. In America, an expression of sympathy was brief and polite, never overbearing. Life was not a Russian novel; here people weren't so much into eternal suffering and your interest in someone's affairs should not extend past a glass of wine and a warm, insouciant remark—"Really? Sorry to hear that. You don't say."

And yet, Carmen can't help her next question. "What did it feel like to grow up without a mother?"

"Like you're the oldest person in the room." Josh pauses to refill his cup. "You're your own ancestor. You feel exposed, unprotected. And you're always looking, always speculating. She could be my mother or she, or maybe that lady with tattoos and a cigarette hanging out of her mouth, or maybe that one on TV, who drowned her six children and I was the lucky one, the one who got away."

"I'm sorry," Carmen says. "It's terrible."

"Yep. But it could've been worse. I could've been aborted." He gives Carmen a shy smile and waves at the flight attendant for another beer.

They begin serving food, and the cabin fills with greasy smells, but Carmen isn't the least bit hungry. She peers out the window at the vermilion sky. It seems as though they are flying through the heart of the universe. She remembers how, during the two months that her mother stayed with her, in a cluttered one-bedroom apartment in Miami Beach, she insisted on buying groceries and cooking since restaurants were so unjustifiably expensive and Carmen subsisted on protein shakes, chips and salsa. Once, however, right before her mother's return to Moscow, the two of them ate in a narrow, bullet-shaped diner converted from an old trolley car in the Art Deco district, where buildings resembled stage decorations or movie props. The food was cheap and all-American—turkey, stuffing, mashed potatoes, gravy. To Carmen's surprise, her mother devoured everything on her plate. On the way back, they bought ice cream, strolling along Lincoln Road, waffle cones in hand, recalling the taste of a Russian *plombir*.

As they reached the beach, they took off their shoes and stepped on the warm sand, skirting around a few roped-off turtles' nests, tracing the shoreline, their footprints filling with water, washing away. The sun was red, like the pulp of a watermelon, glowing low in the evening sky. Her mother stopped and eyed a mangrove, with its massive exposed roots bogging in the sand, and then peered into the glazed depth of the ocean, cocking her head, squinting. "The water is always the same," she said. "Always beautiful."

* * *

At Domodedovo Airport, Josh helps Carmen with the luggage, offering to share a cab. But Carmen declines, saying that they'll be heading in opposite directions, although it isn't entirely true—she could've dropped him off at his hotel and then proceeded home. She does write his number down, out of courtesy.

Riding in the cab, Carmen notes new buildings cased in glass, mirroring one another in the mid-afternoon sun. They are liquid, mercurial structures, not much different from the ones in Miami. She drives by billboards flashing with the same beautiful mawkish faces, by birch groves and farmers' markets, by kiosk stands where you can buy any ridiculous thing at any godforsaken hour. Despite some of its recent remodeling, the city looks crippled; the older, poorer districts lie gutted at her feet, their entrails exposed on the hot, dust-caked asphalt. She thinks of Miami, which is so unlike Moscow—a perpetual holiday, a feast of scantily-clad bodies and tanned shimmery skin, life's eternal glow.

At some point during her mother's visit five years ago, Carmen drove her to the mall, although her mother insisted that she needed nothing, except maybe bras. So they shopped for bras, which was just as excruciating as anything they did together. It took her mother hours to wade through the Macy's lingerie department, Carmen dogging after her. She'd seen her mother naked countless times; she'd know it was her mother's body even if it had no head. Carmen shuddered at the thought. But standing behind her mother in the dressing room, looking in the mirror—her parched breasts bared under the harsh fluorescent lighting—Carmen grew aware of how much time had passed since those summers in the country, as well as of how much time had passed between the two of them.

In the mirror, her mother's body was a display of years and gravity, her withering nakedness a testament to Carmen's own age, suddenly making her uncomfortable, filled with pity. She pressed her hands to her chest, as though shielding herself from an invisible someone in the mirror, and stepped out of the dressing room. Her mother had picked out five bras but couldn't decide which one to buy, and Carmen, without even looking at their prices, paid for all of them.

* * *

When Carmen arrives at her old flat, it's still daylight, but the hallway is tomb-dark, and as soon as she steps across the threshold, she has sensed it—the change in the air, the frigid permanency to it. Leezy doesn't come out to greet her, so Carmen prowls along a narrow corridor, discovering her sister in the kitchen, kneading dough for pierogies.

"The funeral is Saturday," she says, not so much to Carmen but to herself. "I have to make all the food. The neighbors will help with the rest. We need to find another pallbearer. Maybe you could call one of your old boyfriends." She sweeps her gray hair away from her face, but it falls back, the tips brushing the dough.

Carmen thinks of Josh, then asks, "Where is she? Which morgue?" Her lips barely move, just parting wide enough to let the air pass.

"She's here, in her bed. Yesterday, I tried to persuade her to go to the hospital. But she refused. It just happened this morning. I called twenty morgues—no one has any space. It's been very hot. Lots of deaths." Leezy continues kneading the dough.

"So she's going to lie here for two days?" Carmen asks, the words falling from her mouth like beach pebbles, hitting the floor.

"I called a private mortician. He'll be here in a few hours. We'll have to wash and dress the body." Leezy frees her hands from the dough and wipes her cheeks with their mother's old apron, tied loosely around her waist. Only now does Carmen notice how flushed and puffy Leezy's face is, wet from tears, sweat. Two deep lines surround Leezy's mouth, her skin sandy-yellow. She hasn't gained any weight, but seems thicker, heavier. There's something irrefutable in her expression and fragile too—a shell pried open. She's her mother's daughter, but also her own self, with limited experience of life and men, of anything really, except books.

"Can't we pay the mortician to wash her?" Carmen ventures to ask. "I mean wouldn't that be the smart thing to do? Natural?"

"Natural?" her sister repeats, stretching the syllables.

"Yeah. In America, funeral homes take care of everything."

"We aren't in America, so you can drop your fancy. I'll do everything myself."

"How are you going to get her to the bathroom?" Carmen pulls the chair out and sits down. She feels tired and jetlagged, starved too. Her mother's absence hasn't yet affected her, become irrevocable, solidified. She keeps turning her head toward the door, expecting their mother to sail into the kitchen like a cruise ship.

"Not *her*, but our mother, Carmen. Our mother. The one who gave birth to you."

Carmen raises her eyes. "I thought she only gave birth to you, and I was the afterbirth. A defective condom. An accident."

Leezy picks up the dough from the table, squishing it through her fingers. "Why are you so—"

"So—what?"

"Unrelenting. Unaccepting."

"What's there to accept? That she loved you more than she did me? That she protected you, petted you, worried about you?"

"She worried about you, too, Carmen."

"Not so much."

"You're the one who left."

"And you're the one who stayed. I'm the bad guy, and you're the good guy. Glad we settled that." Carmen gets up and stomps out of the kitchen, through the dark hallway, past her bloated suitcase and the old coatrack, where her mother's trenchcoat still hangs by the entrance door.

Half an hour later, having smoked a few cigarettes, Carmen creeps back into her mother's apartment. From the hallway, she can hear Leezy filling the tub while talking to her mother, as though she were still alive. She is cooing almost, describing in a soft, confident voice what she's about to do and why she has to do it, like a parent preparing her child for the inevitable. Now she's taking off the soiled clothes, and now she's lifting her up, and now she's placing her in the water, and now she's going to wash her—here and there, everywhere. She says she'll be gentle and fast and thorough, all those things her mother taught her.

Leezy cuts off the water, and Carmen hears a small splash, a low wave crashing ashore. She stands in the dark, head against the wall, imagining her mother's body sunk to the bottom of the tub, eyes closed, chin low, hair wavering like seaweed fingers. She imagines Leezy picking up a coral-shaped sponge and lathering her mother's arms, one at a time, her caved-in chest, and under the breasts, small, shriveled, fitting in the cups of Leezy's hands, and then the heavy slopes of her mother's stomach, her thighs tracked with veins and stretch marks, drawing the sponge farther down the pale legs, reaching the feet, the hardened tips of her toes.

* * *

At night, Carmen can't sleep. She curls on the living room couch surrounded by shadows that creep over the walls and the tall sagging bookshelves. What kind of books are they? How many? Has her sister read them all? Carmen remembers how as children they spent their summers in the country with their grandparents, staying at their dacha—a small cottage painted blue and constantly being worked on. How they lay awake, listening to crickets chirp behind an old woodstove or gazing at the full moon like a gorgeous pendant suspended from a limb of an aspen tree. They made crazy wishes with serious, adult faces: "When I grow up, I'll marry the Prince of Wales." "And I'll become a ballerina and dance at the Bolshoi." When Leezy turned eighteen, Carmen was eight, but most of the time Carmen felt just as tall and smart as her sister. She even tried to read her books, flipping through pages of romance novels packed with forbidden love. Carmen didn't quite understand what it meant—if it's love, why was it forbidden?—so she kept searching for words or scenes that would explain to her the mystery of a broken heart which, too, made little sense. If it's a heart, how could you break it?

Their mother came every weekend; their father didn't come at all. After the divorce, his visits shrank to once a month to none. When their parents lived together, they fought and often in front of the children. Their father accusing their mother of being too controlling and stubborn, impossible to live with; their mother repeating the same question over and over again, "Who is she? Who is she? Who?"

At the dacha, all those fights had seemed far away, replaced by thunderstorms and the crackling of logs in the woodstove. Carmen ran wild through meadows and coppices, fields of prickly wheat, while Leezy sat on a blanket by the river, reading books. On occasion, Carmen tried on Leezy's bras, stuffing her small fists inside the cups to make them look full, Leezy turning red, snatching her bras out of her sister's hands. Sometimes, Leezy played tricks on Carmen, burying her dolls in a pile of manure behind the house. Carmen, in turn, tore and burned pages out of Leezy's books, the pages that seemed to have important dialogue or scenes, without which the reader would never get to the heart of things. "Things aren't supposed to have hearts," Carmen told Leezy. And Leezy said, "You are the one without a heart. Why did you have to destroy those books? Go away and don't come back. You aren't my sister anymore."

Leezy's words had tortured Carmen no end. Once, she woke up in the middle of the night and tiptoed to Leezy's bed, peering at her sister's face that was so unlike Carmen's, long and pale and freckled. "I'm still your sister," she whispered in Leezy's ear, then slunk back into bed and toiled to go to sleep. Outside, trees shivered in the wind. Their tangled limbs scraped the glass, reminding Carmen of witches' hands, bony and crooked, with curved purple fingernails. She thought she saw a woman's face pressed against the window, her hair a collage of leaves soggy from rain. Lightning flashed and the face dissipated, leaving a trace of fog on the glass.

* * *

The funeral is a small, private affair, attended by a few neighbors and relatives. As it turns out, their mother didn't have many friends, most either had died or were too sick or too old for such joyless gatherings. To find another pallbearer, Carmen first wanted to phone their father, but Leezy rejected the idea on the grounds that their mother would've never allowed the man who didn't love her in life to pity her in death. Carmen acquiesced; she knew her mother's pride and her will, which could have forced waters to part open and fish to swim backwards. She resolved to ask Josh, despite her initial reservations and uneasiness about imposing on a total stranger.

He arrives at their flat thirty minutes ahead of time and is dressed accordingly—a black suit, a white shirt, and a gray-and-white striped tie. He's freshly shaved, but still has a beach smell about him, a hint of grain and salt, although very fine. Carmen can't help but admire his posture and promptness, the way he carries himself in the face of grief and foreign circumstance. His manners are business-like, calm and focused, and yet there's a welcoming softness in his expression, the implied understanding of loss beyond sentiment. He hugs her and gives her flowers, a bouquet of five white lilies, from which Carmen plucks one, breaks off its head, and inserts it into the slit of his lapel.

"The number of flowers for funerals has to be even," she says in English, fitting the lilies in a vase. "And odd for all the other occasions. Not that you need to remember that."

"I do, if I want to see you again."

His honesty isn't new or shocking, but pleasant, an extended invitation to which Carmen doesn't have to respond until much later, if ever. He speaks very little Russian, so he can't communicate with anyone except through Carmen, and she introduces him to several relatives and her sister. Leezy wears a black sleeveless dress that turns her skin pallid white and exacerbates the deep lines around her mouth. Her hair is braided and arranged on the back of her head in an intricate old-fashioned style, like the one their mother wore. As always, she has no makeup; her cheeks are pasty, the eyes two dark wet pits. Freckles crowd her nose and her shoulders, and Carmen is surprised her sister still has them.

"Thanks for coming," Leezy tells Josh, and Carmen translates.

"No problem. Of course. I'm honored your sister thought of me." Again, Carmen translates, but Leezy doesn't let her finish and strays into the kitchen, leaving Carmen to pause mid-sentence.

"She's upset. Too much on her," Josh says.

Carmen nods as her gaze switches to an older couple on the couch holding hands. They sit too close to each other as though they're pressed for room or for air, which is hot and stiff, heavy too, weighing on Carmen's shoulders like rain clouds, years and years of arguments that must turn to water and then to dust. All of a sudden, an image surges—her walking through the woods with Leezy and their mother. Carmen must've been ten or eleven, they were gathering wild mushrooms for soup. They strayed too far, the dachas were no longer visible, and no sound could reach them but the birch trees catching limbs and shedding leaves that twirled about as Carmen tried to grab a few. She tripped over a cluster of roots and fell, twisted her ankle, thrashing and wailing, inconsolable. It was getting dark, the air humid, the sky swollen with clouds. The storm was gathering above the village, and far in the distance, through a thicket of tall slender trees, they could see a flash of lightning splitting the horizon. They took turns carrying her on their backs—Leezy and their mother—Carmen's spindly arms and legs wrapped around their hunched bodies. She would ask them to stop, to rest, to wait until someone came by and helped them. But their mother would not. "You're as light as a feather," she would say again and again, adjusting Carmen higher on her back. "A small, beautiful, graceful feather."

Carmen experiences a peculiar tightness in her chest, and then a sharp pain and a thickening of air. She breathes in and out, unbuttons her blouse, revealing a triangle of tan skin below the sharp collarbones, a thumb-wide space between her breasts. She presses on it and massages clockwise and then reverses the direction. She steps closer to the window, which is open, the sunrays sneaking through tree branches. The leaves are still green, with threads of purplish-red, like the veins on their mother's hands. Carmen's throat is parched, scratchy. She misses Miami—the lights, the beach, the ocean. All its immeasurable vastness and depth, the feel of wet shifting sand under her feet.

Josh walks up to her and stands right behind, his hand on her shoulder. He squeezes lightly, and Carmen reaches up and pats it. His fingers are strong, smooth, with round, almost feminine fingernails. Carmen has the urge to hold on to those fingers, to feel them touch her body in a dark room, with nothing visible, nothing at all. The sun, the heat is making her dizzy; her skin blazes under the makeup. She's dressed in a black shirt and a matching pencil skirt that ends right above her knees. "Too short," her mother would've said. "Too short, and too tight."

The casket is at the far end of the room, placed on their ancient dining table, with pleats of red fabric gathered around the base like a full-length skirt. Next to the table, the lid, also draped in red, leans against the wall, with a large three-barred cross stitched in golden silk. The casket is a simple, delicate construction and doesn't resemble the formidable American versions Carmen encountered in Miami, but it's the fanciest, most expensive arrangement they could find on such short notice, and Carmen paid for it. As well as for the mortician, the flowers, and the crematorium services. They decided against a preacher since their mother never attended church or believed in any omnipresent force or will stronger than her own. Leezy tried to share the expenses, but Carmen wouldn't oblige—it was the least she could do. There was a frown on her sister's face, then a scoff, all melting into tears, torrents of incoherent mumble.

"We have a problem," Leezy whispers in her ear. Carmen trembles and shifts her head.

"What is it?" she asks.

"It's too hot, and she's begun to thaw."

"To thaw?"

"The makeup on her face has melted, and you can see the bruises, where she fell, but also some bloody discharge from the mouth and in the corner of one eye. I don't know what to do."

Carmen twists her hair at the roots, musses the bangs. "Shit," she says. "Shit."

"What's wrong?" Josh asks. He continues to stand beside Carmen, but his hand is off her shoulder.

"Our mother is a snow maiden, melting under the sun," Carmen says, perhaps a bit loud. "Do you know that story? There's an opera too. Rimsky-Korsakov."

"I haven't heard the opera, but I read the story."

"Shit," Carmen says. "Where will we find another mortician now?"

Josh pinches his chin, then rubs his thumb up and down his lips "What kind of makeup do you have?" he asks. "Perhaps I can help. I know a lot about faces."

Carmen rushes to translate each word to Leezy, who offers to ask the neighbors for more cosmetics.

In a short while, the mourners are being ushered into the kitchen while Josh arranges tubes of concealers and foundation, tinted moisturizers, small cups of cornstarch and white flour on the table, next to the casket. Carmen delivers primers and two types of blush, powder compacts and a bronzer, lipsticks, glosses, brow pencils and eye shadows. A set of weathered brushes in a jar. Their mother is dressed in a beige linen suit and a white satin shirt without a collar but two diaphanous strips of fabric tied into a lush bow. Her face hasn't changed much, yet it does appear hard and brittle, as though carved out of ice. She has no jewelry on except for an old gold watch she rarely took off while alive. Neither Carmen nor Leezy wanted to keep the watch, and Carmen regrets it. She will probably never wear it, but the thought of taking the relic to Miami along with half of her mother's ashes brings on a feeling of unexplained comfort and longing, something she hopes she can share with Leezy later tonight.

As Josh shrugs off his jacket and rolls up the shirtsleeves, the sisters stand on the other side of the table, with wads of tissues and cotton in their hands. Carmen thinks they look like nurses assisting a plastic surgeon who's deft and impassioned and determined. Josh smooths the hair away from their mother's face and tucks a few snowy strands behind her ears, exposing a large bruise above the right temple and another a bit lower, on her jaw. He examines the rest of the face and under the sharp chin. His movements are swift, feathery, almost imperceptible, as though he isn't tending to a dead body but to an ungoverned spirit that Carmen imagines hovering about the room. Both she and Leezy don't breathe a sound as they watch Josh work, carefully, meticulously, touching and retouching the dead flesh, massaging the stiffened folds, patting, stroking, buffing, bringing a warm glow back to the lifeless cheeks. Under his persistent fingers, their mother's skin transforms, acquires a burst of sunshine spilling onto Josh's hands.

For just a moment, Carmen is distracted by the tree limbs swaying behind the window, a pandemonium of leaves. There's also a face, a child's face, looming through a plexus of branches and sunrays. The girl's lips press against the glass, open and close silently, like those of a doll. She is telling Carmen something—a tale perhaps—something sad and beautiful and unknown.

Semi-Finalist
Madelyn Garner

Surgical Mask in the Time of Plagues

Half my face erased, only eyes
above horizon — unmoored
from a crooked nose,
muffled mouth.

The nurses insist I wear a mask —
white as blisters,
as bone, as mausoleum marble.

Snow fort.

What have other mothers done
in times like these:

Remain hidden in their homes?

Come swaddled
in gown and booties, blue-gloved?

Or do some of them attend, defiant —
faces bare?

For days I have kissed my son
through paper —
sail billowing with each exhale.

Now watching him again turn away
from me as if a stranger,

I choose —
remove the mask.

Enough

I wake this morning thinking of a son cut off
at mid-blossom,
but dawn's garden is insistent:

Come, the plum trees are fruiting—
violet-green pendants swelling toward sweetness—

hummingbirds spangle in earth's early light.

Even the saw-toothed sunflowers are ticking their way toward multiplying.

I stand knee-deep among
ox-eye, star-studded yarrow, prairie coneflower in this place where

the grass from yesterday's rain-drench
presses against the gate of my head for a way in—

to smooth out grief, cover it,
bury under.

The Mask

She kept the mask, not knowing
what to do with it. That hard plastic skin
molded to the shape of his face, fitted over
his head and attached to the treatment table.
It sits in a coffee-maker box
on the closet shelf above the shoes
she's kept as well, though all the clothes
are gone. She tells no one. It's been three years —
her friends and son wouldn't understand.

Tonight she drops his shoes in a garbage bag,
relaxes her gaze, something she's learned
to do in yoga so she doesn't really see.
Then she takes down the box that promises
Maximum Capacity, Brew Strength Control,
Easy-to-Fill Water Reservoir.

She opens the lid: there it is, his face —
an empty husk, cut-outs for the mouth and nose,
none for the eyes. When asked if he wanted them,
he'd said no. She thought he'd made that choice
so he wouldn't see the blank expression
of the radiographer, the cold machine
that promised nothing. Later she wondered if,
in some strange way, he was getting ready.
Not only lying still but blind now, too,
the table sliding him headfirst into a fire.

He'd practiced death so well,
when she brought him home, she kept checking
with a feather, an owl's white down.
As a singer, he'd learned to turn a single breath
into so much sound it filled their church.
It undermined the light.

More than any photograph taken near the last,
the cast holds his likeness. She runs her fingers over

his nose, the shells of his ears, his jaw's parentheses.
What disturbs her most is the mouth, the hope-
lessness of the opening his lips surround.

She lies down on what she calls *their* bed
and dons the mask. It doesn't fit, of course,
her face is small inside it. Three years.
She trembles under the duvet that must be
stuffed with snow. Her eyes won't open.

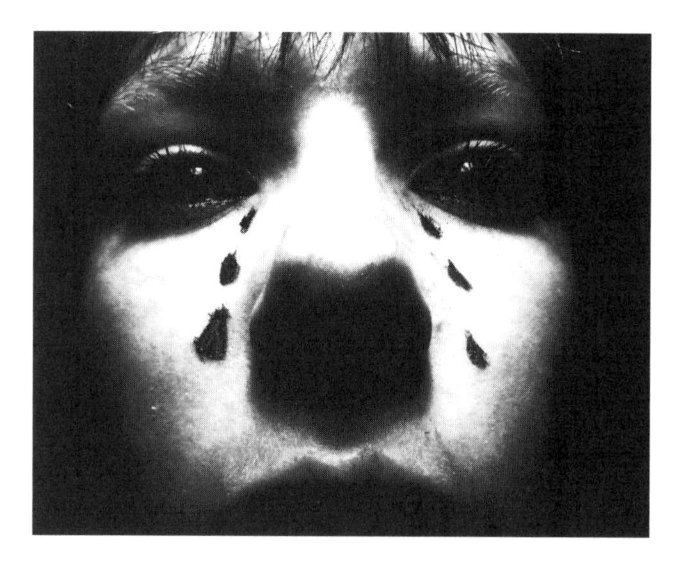

Eleanor Leonne Bennett, photograph

Landslide in Florida

Now we can watch the sandhill cranes' stately steps
across our lawn. December, and the only ice
is in our tea. We go shopping in our golf cart.
I read novels on our lanai. Often
I glance up to see you look at me while you wait
for your memories and words to connect,
but the bands that hold them together
have stretched, my love, they're breaking.
With words that fall in the pattern
of dominoes dropped on a tabletop,
you talk of a drive you once made
            somewhere for
                                    something
                  you can't   quite   name.
As I eat my breakfast grapefruit, you struggle
to remember *milk* goes on the cornflakes,
juice goes in the *glass*.
You pursue new interests:
you build tiny piles of crumbs,
you pluck lint from the placemat.
The life we've known clings to the side of a hill
in heavy rain. We strain to hold the turf in place
but pieces slide away, rearrange. Scars appear.
It's hard to see in this new landscape
a thing of beauty. We're tumbling
in the rubble. We're picking up crumbs.
We're building new piles together.

My Mother Turns Ninety

She's so thin her wedding ring
slips off her finger and she begins

passing it from one hand to the other.
She says she wants to move my father's grave

so she can be buried between
both her husbands. Really?

My father died at 29.
In the house of my childhood

there wasn't one photo of him,
not on a bureau, not on a desk,

not in the picture case in her wallet.
He was a secret saved for night,

when she sat on my bed and rubbed my back,
whispering stories—

she met him when he was a lifeguard,
all the girls wanted him,

they drove all night to see the sun rise
from Brooklyn Bridge. *Dick,*

she called him, and I did, too.
Her next husband I called Father

for fifty years. From the street below
lights of moving cars beckon

like a movie scene. Here in the apartment
I'm lulled by the back-and-forth,

the slight pause of the ring
as it settles in her palm

before the gold darts, again,
to the other hand.

Todd Camp, *Look Away, Hey Watch This,* acrylic, collage, and encaustic on canvas, 12" x 12"

Painter's Mother IV

after Lucian Freud

stares at an unseen object
perhaps on a table just out of reach.
A slight frown gathers between brows raised quizzically.

She is old and cannot understand why
she is a suitable subject for portraiture, but this is not the first
question she does not ask her son.

Her hair loosely tied back, rebellious strands escape,
falling behind her neck, her torso covered by a sweater that leaks
brown onto her jaw-line and the pockets of her cheeks.

Is it resignation or impatience that has thrust her onto this chair
in front of a background swathed in more brown and a stripe of gray?
After all she has put up with, she deserves color, a red flower

splotched on a lapel, a gnarl of purple yarn to occupy her hands.
But this is what they do to old people, forcing them to pull a chair
to a window as if any view will satisfy.

Hobbled

Wind shears across the shorn field, and three willows
are walking, picking their way
          among the stubble.
                    They raise, lower, then raise their arms,
like children pretending to be birds. But they cannot

see where they are going, blind trees,
          tapping their canes between flutters,
rattling their twiggy cloaks, reciting nursery rhymes

to keep the cougars with their claws away.
                    The rise and fall, the hobbledy-hoy,
the mumbledy-peg of their walking,

three willows giving up, leaving
                              the parched basin, their ancestral home;

three blind trees not running
          after the farmer's wife but hobbled
with their news: the dwindling rains

                    and poisoned seeds, the treacherously
innocent pollen the bees,

                    the determined bees,
          will surely gather.

Emigration

So many reasons for leaving,
water grown foul and brackish,
potatoes freshly dug, already
the color of stone. The aroma
of food drew us away,
how our mouths watered
in our dreams! On the ship
we begin with soup, like the gentry,
or a small bird, grouse
or pigeon, then roast mutton,
new potatoes, tender green peas.

Spoilage is our cargo, provisions
in straw baskets gone damp and soft.
The ship's rats dine well on bags of flour
and kegs that dribble in the hold.
Every night another villager slips
into the accepting sea, a tablespoon of earth pressed
into the palm before the fingers freeze in death.
Now sailors sing their makeshift prayers
that the body will find some firm place,
the soul keep on swimming.

SEMI-FINALIST
KIM GARCIA

Householder

I have aged whole days by a sea eating away at the shore
and watched the cliffside houses, year by year, kneel
                                        after winter's storms

slowly, painfully towards the rocks. I've heard the stories too:
In one a murder, in the next a child born. Once in this house a woman
                                        no longer so young or sure

mended her restless son's shirt—while he stood holding
one foot, barechested, balancing on one skinny brown leg because
                                        he is eight, and he can.

His mother reaches up without looking and turns on the lamp.
That is her small human business—a single switch, like the sheering
                                        of a gull's wing as it turns.

Her house lights up, meeting dusk at the glass, cheering the cove perhaps,
with lighthouse gleam—while the domestic needle, a fine silver fishbone, pierces
                                        fiercely again and again.

Prophets

The coal goes out before it touches my tongue
but the ravens still feed me
it was laudanum that dulled Poe
to the medicine
in that poison—*ever more*
within the bird's prophecy
and even, for the hungry-hearted:
more, more, more
from the black lobster claw
of that ruthless beak

In Which I Praise My Right Foot

Hours ago, the technician asked, What's your mother's maiden name?
handed me a heavy apron and disappeared.
Now I stare at the screen. Pale bones against the dark.
Like watching a sneak preview of myself as a skeleton.
And I'm amazed. I love looking at my bones.
There's the metatarsal leading to the skewed phalanges of the great toe,
the bony bump on the joint between them. The metatarsophalangeal joint.
I hear a tap at the door. In walks a man
who looks so much younger than my sons.
He takes my bare right foot in his hands, gently touches each toe.
Two curled toes. Two hammertoes. Below the great toe, one bunion.
And, on the other side, at the base of the little toe, a bunionette.
I think, What a mess. He says, You must be right-footed.
I always start with that foot. There you are, he says.
As if everything has just been explained.
Often surgery is no help, he tells me.
I'll live with it, I say. He smiles. I've given the right answer.
Did your mother have bunions?
I slide a sock over the one I've named my witch's foot,
imagine brewing a potion, feeling the spoon slip, the splash of liquid
that makes me a true witch, marked by my own magic.
Once home, I begin throwing out shoes.
The heels I bought in London during the last winter of my marriage.
How did my feet ever fit into them?
After the divorce, the boots I took trekking with my sons in Nepal.
Which I had on the day I met my partner, who later said,
because they were worn, he knew we had a lot in common.
I work my way deeper into the closet. Why did I need
the pumpkin-colored slip-ons, the turquoise and purple Mary Janes,
the elegant tall boots I hardly used? Their glove-soft leather.
I fill bag after bag. Soon, other witches will join me.
All of us, lopsided. The time of symmetry, over. But now what?
We'll dance a crooked dance around an ancient fire, chant our bones,
our deformities, our mothers' maiden names, and, as we turn,
I'll step forward on my right foot, into the inscrutable future.

Cleaning Up

After I spent hours
untangling wires unplugged at both ends,
moving the unused VCR and uncabled TV,
dusting and stacking the ancient CDs,

the floor appeared for the first time
in a very long time, making it possible
to vacuum the startled rug,
though the bigger surprise

was how annoyed I felt
at the room's sudden sparkle and bounce,
the way it had returned to almost new,
no longer burdened by the irrelevant,

the unnecessary, the dusty old rules:
be nice,
think of others,
shhh—keep your voice down.

Orchard Orb-Weaver

Having strung one orb she felt compelled
to waltz concentric rings around it, ripple

the gap between broad leaf and blossom, weave
a curtain out of air. Backdrop done,

she rappelled on silk to a spot in the sun and posed
against the grid, a glint on a drape,

red-specked and yellow-flecked abdomen
making me recoil quickly.

Hourglass-marked or not, she had to be a widow
or recluse or poet or hacker

or some other dangerous loner—
or so I figured, forgetting that bright women

merit an Internet search, not a panicked squashing.
I who spent hours humming at the sewing machine,

cutting circles of velveteen, pinning strips of piping,
tore my own karmic fabric when I leaned into the ginger plant

and clapped the pretty artist between two boards.
Only after did I check the web and learn her name

and the harmlessness of her venom. Now I've lost my thread;
the tension is wrong and the stitches bunch

and I question my craftsmanship. In public, I'm wary of glistening;
I won't wear a bold print when I go out dancing.

Welcome

Everything you thought you knew
must be relearned overnight.

How to walk.
Walk, not trip, over cords, 2 X 4s,
used coffee cups, concrete cores.
Walk, 40 pounds on your shoulder, across
rebar or a wood plank; glide,
not wobble, not look like the bounce
beneath each bootstep scares you.

How to dress yourself
to work outdoors all day midwinter
and keep warm, keep working, fingers moving;
or midsummer, with no hint of breasts.

How to climb ladders—
not a stepstool or 4-footer—
ladders that stretch up two stories
where someone's impatient
for that bundle of pipe.

How to get coffee—
hot and how they like it—to a crew
spread out 10 floors; to carry muffins
three blocks in a paper sack
through sheets of rain.

How to look.
How you don't go back empty-handed
when you're told, *Grab me a This/That
from the gangbox*, if all you've done
is move things around, poke here and there;
if you haven't emptied out the full contents
so the journeyman won't shame you
by finding that This/That in a quick minute,
after you've said, *We don't have any*.

How to be dependable
but not predictable-provokable.
Not the lunch-break entertainment.

How to read
blueprints,
delivery orders,
the mood on the job;
how long it's okay to sit down for coffee;
how early you can start rolling up cords.

How to do well in school
from the back row
of a seats-assigned-Jim-Crow classroom.
How to learn tricks of the trade
from someone who does not like you.

How to listen,
how to act-don't-ask.
To duck when someone motions, *Duck!*
Or when someone tells you, *Don't talk to Zeke,*
you know what they mean
and you don't even look
at Zeke, the ironworker who's always first out,
last in, standing there, so four times a day—
start, lunch, quit—all the workers walk past him.
Like a sandbar—waves washing back and forth—
that catches debris.

How to pick up the phone and call your friend,
the only one of the women not at class
the night the apprenticeship director met you all
at the door
carrying the nervous rumor
that one of the women had been raped
and you all look at each other
and it wasn't any of you five.

How to behave.
Protocols for when someone
takes your ladder or tools;
imitates your voice on the loudspeaker;
spraypaints *Cunt* on your Baker staging;
urinates in your hardhat;
drives to your home
where you live alone
with your daughter
and keys your truck parked
in your own driveway.

Later, you'll need the advanced skills:
how—without dislodging the keystone—
to humiliate a person,
how to threaten a person. Deftly.
So no one's certain for absolute
that's what happened. Not even you.

Angels of Recycling

In the chilly tin buildings
shoved up against each other
and fastened together by drafts,
a half-dozen half-paid helpers
are sorting and stacking
the aluminum storm doors,
sour toilets, ceiling panels,
and stone-hard bags of ready-mix.

Name whatever you're looking for,
a faucet, a can of latex primer,
a garbage disposal that works,
and somebody, maybe a thin
recycled girl with yellow gloves,
a steel stud in her tongue,
and a jacket too thin for the weather,
will show you where to find it.

But you're free to become a part
of it all, to wander the aisles
with the others, measuring windows,
pawing through half-full bins
of doorknobs cold as snowballs,
boxes of vinyl flooring tile,
bundles of cove and molding,
rolls of carpet choked with rope.

And to nod a hello to a man
who suddenly appears before you,
stepping out of the shadows, out of
the ALL FOR SALE and AS IS,
wearing a coat of many colors
and bearing a fiery curtain rod,
two blocks from the City Mission,
and close to the Burlington tracks.

The Albino Turkey

She makes her appearance out at the edge
of whatever I'm doing. She's like something
I've tried to remember but keep forgetting,
just a glimpse of whatever it was. Not quite
a true albino, either, part white, part gray,
like a dried-out milkweed pod, come limping
in and out of the tall grass next to the pond
or bobbing through shadows under the lilacs,
keeping her distance. Always alone, surviving
the coyotes, the dogs, her lame left leg,
shunned, I suppose, by the flock. A more thrilling
survival, or so it feels to me, than anyone
going over the falls in a barrel or climbing out
of a coffin after the magician has plucked
the swords away. But just a turkey, really,
only a turkey, dumb as a barrel of hair,
picki ng her way through the world.

Testing, Testing

I dust off my voice, which is like the lid
of an old upright piano, its varnish
a webwork of cracks, its music
still hanging in cold metal curtains
far down inside. *Testing*, the word
feels its way into the dark auditorium,
over the empty faces of the seats,
over their knees pulled up and clasped
so a custodian can reach the notes
dropped from whoever was speaking
the last time, always the last time,
the last chance, the last words.
With hope I kiss the microphone's
cold knuckle, wanting its blessing,
while my one frail prayer, *Testing, testing*,
reaches out to the only generosity
present, that warm yellow rectangle
far in the back, that little window
behind which an engineer sits
doing his best to make me better,
editing fear from my voice, adjusting
the knobs on the front of my heart.

HEATHER ALTFELD is the author of *The Disappearing Theatre* (forthcoming, 2015, from Poets at Work Press). She has recently discovered the virtues of a hammock. She lives and writes in a little rural corner of Chico, California, and her recent poems can be found in *Narrative Magazine, Poetry Northwest, Pleiades, The Literary Review, Zyzzyva*, and elsewhere.

MICHELLE COLLINS ANDERSON's short stories have appeared in *Midwestern Gothic, Literary Mama, Green Hills Literary Lantern*, and *The Sulphur River Literary Review*. She received her M.F.A. from Warren Wilson College and lives with her husband and three children in Liberty, Missouri, where she teaches creative writing at Franklin Elementary. She also serves on the board of *The Missouri Review*.

WENDY BARKER's sixth collection, *One Blackbird at a Time: The Teaching Poems*, has been chosen for the John Ciardi Prize and will be published by BkMk Press, fall 2015. Her fourth chapbook, *From the Moon, Earth is Blue*, is also due in fall 2015, from Wings Press. Her poetry has appeared in numerous journals and anthologies, including *Best American Poetry 2013*. Recipient of National Endowment for the Arts and Rockefeller fellowships, she teaches at University of Texas, San Antonio.

DENNIS BRADEN has an M.A. in English Literature from University of Colorado, Boulder. He has taken part in a writing residency with the Edward F. Albee Foundation, and his poetry appears in *Bellingham Review, Caveat Lector, The Chattahoochee Review, Confrontation Magazine, Dacotah Territory, Eleven, FORUM, J Journal, Star*Line*, and other journals. He has a chapbook, *In Things Completed*, published by Konglomerati Press of Florida.

SARA BURANT is the author of the chapbook *Verge*. Her work has appeared in *Poetry East, Cloudbank*, and *Christianity & Literature*. She lives in Eugene, Oregon.

SARAH CARLETON writes, edits, plays music, and homeschools her son in Tampa, Florida. Her poems have appeared in *houseboat, Burningword Literary Journal, Avatar Review, Poetry Quarterly, The Bijou Poetry Review, Off the Coast*, and *Wild Violet*. She has work forthcoming in *Cider Press Review* and is an honoree in this year's *Binnacle* Ultra-Short Competition.

STEPHANIE CARPENTER's work has appeared or is forthcoming in *Crab Orchard Review, The Cossack Review, Storyscape, Quiddity International Literary Journal, Big Fiction Magazine,* and elsewhere. She teaches literature and creative writing at Michigan Tech University. She is currently at work on a pair of novellas about female artists in nineteenth-century New England.

LEILA CHATTI is a Tunisian-American poet and former special education teacher. She received her M.F.A. in poetry from North Carolina State University and is a winner of an Academy of American Poets Prize. Her work appears in journals such as *Rattle, Linebreak,* and *decomP*. She currently serves on the poetry staff at *The Adroit Journal.*

JENNIFER CLARK lives in Kalamazoo, Michigan. Her first book of poems, *Necessary Clearings,* was recently published by Shabda Press. Her work has been published in such places as *failbetter, Fiction Fix, Windhover, Concho River Review, Structo,* and *The Midwest Quarterly.*

PATRICIA CLARK is Poet-in-Residence and professor in the Department of Writing at Grand Valley State University in Michigan and the author of four volumes of poetry. Her latest book is *Sunday Rising*. Her work has been featured on *Poetry Daily* and *Verse Daily* and also appears in *The Atlantic Monthly, The Gettysburg Review, Poetry, Slate,* and *Stand*. New work is forthcoming in *The Kenyon Review, New England Review,* and *Southern Humanities Review*. She was a semi-finalist for the 36th *Nimrod* Awards.

EMILY ROSE COLE is an M.F.A. candidate in poetry at Southern Illinois University Carbondale. She is the winner of numerous national poetry awards, including the Nancy D. Hargrove Editor's Prize, the Janet B. McCabe Poetry Prize, and the Sandy Crimmins Award. Her poetry has appeared or is forthcoming in *Gulf Stream, Weave Magazine, Jabberwock Review, Passages North,* and *Fugue,* among other publications.

MARSHA TRUMAN COOPER holds a B.A. in English from University of California, Davis. She won first prize in the *New Letters* Literary Awards for poetry and received the Bernice Slote Poetry Award from *Prairie Schooner*. Her work has been published in small magazines including *Narrative Magazine, River Styx,* and *Tar River Poetry*. Her second chapbook is titled *A Knot of Worms*.

LORNA CROZIER's poetry will be published in two books in 2015: *The Wrong Cat* and *The Wild in You,* a collaboration with world-renowned photographer Ian McAllister on The Great Bear Rainforest. A resident of Vancouver Island, she's an Officer of the Order of Canada and the recipient of the Governor-General's Award for Poetry.

CAROL V. DAVIS is the author of *Between Storms* (Truman State University Press). She received the T. S. Eliot Prize for *Into the Arms of Pushkin: Poems of St. Petersburg*. She teaches at Santa Monica College, California, and Antioch University, Louisiana. In February 2015 she lectured at Buryatia State University, Ulan-Ude, Siberia.

MELANIE DRANE spent 18 years living in Germany, Austria, Japan, and the U.K., and is now a psychotherapy intern at the Jung Institute of Los Angeles. For three years, she was caregiver for her late sister Melissa, whose massive stroke resulted in aphasia, loss of language function. She is writing a memoir about their experience, called *The Language Orchard*.

SUSAN EISENBERG is a poet, visual artist, and licensed electrician. She is the author of *Perpetual Care* (2014), a poetry book with photographs exploring chronic illness. Previous books include *Blind Spot* and *Pioneering* (poetry), as well as *We'll Call You If We Need You* (nonfiction), selected as a *New York Times* Notable Book. She is a resident artist/scholar at Brandeis University's Women's Studies Research Center.

CATHERINE FREELING worked in theater and as a public school teacher before arriving at poetry. She has been a finalist in contests from *Nimrod, Rattle, and Bellevue Literary Review*, and both finalist and runner-up in *Hunger Mountain*'s. Her poems have also appeared in *Calyx, New Ohio Review, Poet Lore, Women's Review of Books,* and elsewhere.

KIM GARCIA, author of *Madonna Magdalene,* was the recipient of the 2014 Lynda Hull Memorial Prize. Her work has been featured on *The Writer's Almanac,* and has appeared in *Crazyhorse, Mississippi*

Review, Crab Orchard Review, Nimrod, and *Subtropics*, among others. She teaches creative writing at Boston College.

MADELYN GARNER is a retired public school administrator in Denver, Colorado. Her recent work has appeared or is forthcoming in *Best American Poetry 2015, The Florida Review, Nimrod,* and *Slant Magazine*. She is the co-editor of the anthology *Collecting Life: Poets on Objects Known and Imagined,* a Colorado Book Awards Finalist, 2013. She is currently working on a poetry manuscript.

HELEN T. GLENN's poems have appeared in *The Nebraska Review, The American Journal of Nursing, Spoon River Poetry Review, Flint Hills Review,* and other journals. She is a contributor to several anthologies, including *Intensive Care* (University of Iowa Press), *Claiming the Spirit Within* (Beacon Press) and *Orpheus and Company* (The University Press of New England).

ROCHELLE GOLDSTEIN is an editor and writer living in Brooklyn, New York. Her poetry has appeared in *Podium* and in the anthology *Still Against the War.* She is currently working on her second poetry collection and writing a memoir about her mother's secret life.

KRISTINA GORCHEVA-NEWBERRY, a Russian émigrée, has published a variety of stories, essays, and poetry. Her work has recently appeared in *Nimrod, The Southern Review, Rosebud, Southwest Review, The Louisville Review, Confrontation Magazine,* and elsewhere. Her short fiction has been selected as a finalist for multiple awards, including a Pushcart Prize. Her story, *Boys on the Moskva River,* was the first prize winner of *Nimrod*'s 2013 Katherine Anne Porter Prize for Fiction.

LOREN HIGBEE is a writer and a peripatetic. Originally from Utah, he now lives in Iraqi Kurdistan, where he is a professor of English at the American University of Iraq, Sulaimani.

ED HODGES lives with his wife, dog, and motorcycle in Baltimore. He does most of his writing in coffeehouses or at sidewalk cafe tables. Earlier work has appeared under the penname Edward Adams in *Nimrod, Confrontation Magazine, Forge, Harpur Palate, Pearl, Quiddity International Literary Journal,* and other publications.

Ted Kooser served two terms as U. S. Poet Laureate and during his first term won the Pulitzer Prize in poetry. His most recent books are *Splitting and Order,* a collection of poems from Copper Canyon Press (2014), and *The Wheeling Year,* a collection of prose vignettes from University of Nebraska Press (2014). His third book for children, *The Bell in the Bridge,* is forthcoming from Candlewick Press. He lives in rural Nebraska and teaches part-time at The University of Nebraska.

Susanne Kort is a psychotherapist practicing in Jalisco, Mexico. In the U.S. her poetry has appeared in *North American Review, Notre Dame Review, Grand Street, Green Mountains Review, Indiana Review, Seneca Review, The Laurel Review,* and other journals. Her work has also been published in journals in Ireland, England, and Canada.

Zane Kotker was called back to the poetry she'd started with after publishing a handful of novels as well as short stories in *The Antioch Review, Alaska Quarterly Review,* and elsewhere. Her first chapbook, *Old Ladies in the Locker Room and Pool,* won a 2012 Must Read citation from the Massachusetts Center for the Book.

Lisa C. Krueger is a clinical psychologist; she has published three poetry collections with Red Hen Press. Her poems have appeared or are forthcoming in various journals including *Ploughshares, Prairie Schooner,* and *Poet Lore.* She has published articles and interactive journals related to psychology and creativity, and maintains a psychotherapy practice in Pasadena, California.

George Looney has published his eighth book of poetry, *Meditations Before the Windows Fail,* with Lost Horse Press. He also has three previous books, titled *Structures the Wind Sings Through, Monks Beginning to Waltz,* and *A Short Bestiary of Love and Madness.* He founded the B.F.A. in Creative Writing at Penn State Erie, is editor of *Lake Effect,* translation editor of *Mid-American Review,* and co-founder of the Chautauqua Writers' Festival.

Katharyn Howd Machan is the author of 32 collections, the most recent being *Wild Grapes: Poems of Fox* (Finishing Line Press, 2014), and her individual poems have been widely published. Fairy tales have always been a major inspiration for her poetry, and she teaches several courses based on them for the Department of Writing and the Honors Program at New York's Ithaca College.

DAVIS MCCOMBS is the author of two collections of poetry, titled *Ultima Thule* (Yale) and *Dismal Rock* (Tupelo). He directs the Program in Creative Writing and Translation at the University of Arkansas.

GRANT GERALD MILLER was born in Memphis, Tennessee. He currently teaches creative writing at The Independent Publishing Resource Center in Portland, Oregon.

WENDY MNOOKIN is a poet living in Newton, Massachusetts. Her most recent book is *The Moon Makes Its Own Plea* (BOA Editions). Mnookin has taught poetry at Emerson College and Boston College; she currently teaches at Grub Street, a nonprofit writing program in Boston.

BERWYN MOORE is the 2015 winner of the James Dickey Prize. She has also won awards from *Bellevue Literary Review*, *The Pinch Journal*, and *Margie: The American Journal of Poetry*. Her work has been published in *The Southern Review*, *Shenandoah*, *Poetry Northwest*, *JAMA*, and other journals, as well as in two collections, *O Body Swayed* and *Dissolution of Ghosts*. She teaches at Gannon University in Erie, Pennsylvania.

JUDITH PACHT's *Summer Hunger* won the 2011 PEN Southwest Book Award for poetry. A three-time Pushcart nominee, she was first-place winner in the Georgia Poetry Society's Edgar Bowers competition, and her work has been published in numerous anthologies and journals. Recently she has read at the *Los Angeles Times* Festival of Books, at Charleston's Piccolo Spoleto Festival, and read and taught political poetry at Denver's annual LitFest at the Lighthouse.

JENNIFER RAHA earned her M.F.A. in 2013 from the University of North Carolina at Greensboro. Her work is forthcoming in *Borderlands: Texas Poetry Review*, *Salamander*, *Canary*, *The Café Review*, and *SAND*.

DIAN DUCHIN REED has received the Mary Lonnberg Smith Award in Poetry, and her poems have appeared in *Prairie Schooner, Salamander, TriQuarterly,* and many other literary journals. She is the author of a chapbook, *Medusa Discovers Styling Gel* (Finishing Line Press, 2009). Her most recent project is the translation of the *Dao De Jing* into English poetry.

EARL REINEMAN was a finalist for *Nimrod's* 2013 Pablo Neruda Prize for Poetry and a finalist for the 2013 *New Letters* Poetry Prize. He is a past winner of the William Herbert Carruth Poetry Contest. His poems have appeared in *Nimrod, Coal City Review,* and *Poetry Northwest.* He lives in Lawrence, Kansas.

ANN ROBINSON has been published in *The American Literary Review, The Coachella Review, Connecticut Review, Fourteen Hills, Hiram Poetry Review, Natural Bridge, Poet Lore,* and *Whiskey Island,* among others. She is a Marin Arts Council Grantee and a Hofstra University conference scholarship winner. Her poetry book, *Stone Window,* from Bark for Me publications, came out in January 2014.

PENELOPE SCAMBLY SCHOTT is the author of ten full-length poetry books, six chapbooks, and a novel. Her verse biography, *A is for Anne: Mistress Hutchinson Disturbs the Commonwealth,* won an Oregon Book Award for Poetry. Recent books include *Lovesong for Dufur* and *Lillie Was a Goddess, Lillie Was a Whore;* published in 2014 was *How I Became an Historian.* She lives in Portland and Dufur, Oregon, where she teaches a notorious poetry workshop.

DWAINE SPIEKER teaches high school English in Wayne, Nebraska, where he lives with his wife and four children. His first book, *Garden of Stars,* published by All Along Press, won the 2010 Nebraska Book Award, and his second book, *The Way Magellan Must Have Felt,* was recently published by Rogue Faculty Press.

CHARLOTTE STEWART was the director of academic publications at The University of Tulsa and a founding member of the Tulsa Women Writers. A poet and supporter of *Tulsa Studies in Women's Literature* and Council Oak Books, she was Assistant Editor of *Nimrod* and worked with the *James Joyce Quarterly.* She was also Assistant to the Provost of TU. She passed away in 2014.

ANITA SULLIVAN is a poet, essayist, gardener, translator, and retired piano-tuner in Eugene, Oregon. She earned an M.F.A. in Poetry from Pacific Lutheran University and is an emerita founding editor of the poetry-publishing collective Airlie Press, which published her book *Garden of Beasts* in 2010. She has also published two essay collections and is currently working on a young adult fantasy novel.

EMILY VAN KLEY's poems have appeared or are forthcoming in *The Iowa Review, Mississippi Review, Crab Orchard Review*, and *Knockout Literary Magazine*, among other publications. She's a recipient of the *The Iowa Review* Award and the *The Florida Review* Editor's Award, and has contributed to several anthologies, including *Here: Women Writing on Michigan's Upper Peninsula*. She lives in Olympia, Washington.

JEANNE WAGNER is the winner of the 2014 *Hayden's Ferry* 500/500 Prize and the 2014 *Sow's Ear Poetry Review* Award. Her poems have appeared in *The Cincinnati Review, Alaska Quarterly Review, Shenandoah,* and *River Styx*. The author of five collections, she has most recently published *In the Body of Our Lives*, which was released by Sixteen Rivers Press in 2011.

ARNE WEINGART lives in Chicago, where he is the principal of a graphic design firm specializing in identity and way-finding. His work has been nominated for a Pushcart Prize and his book, *Levitation For Agnostics*, was chosen as the 2014 winner of the New American Press Poetry Prize, and will be published in 2015.

J. DUNCAN WILEY's fiction has appeared or is forthcoming in *Best Small Fictions 2015, Pleiades, Cream City Review*, and *South Dakota Review*. He is currently nearing completion of a collection of short stories portraying characters involved in various searches for mineral wealth.

EMILY WORTMAN-WUNDER lives in south suburban Denver, where she explores the meaning of place in a world that often tries to ignore it. She has published fiction and nonfiction in *Seed Magazine, High Country News, Terrain,* and *West Branch,* among others, and has fiction forthcoming in *The Masters Review.*

JOSEPHINE YU's first manuscript, *Prayer Book of the Anxious*, won the Judge's Prize of the 15th Annual Elixir Press Poetry Award and will be published in 2016. Her poems have appeared in such journals as *Ploughshares, The Southern Review, TriQuarterly, Best New Poets 2008, Crab Orchard Review, Bellingham Review, River Styx, New Letters*, and *32 Poems*.

Eleanor Leonne Bennett is an internationally award-winning artist. She is an art editor for multiple publications around the world. Her photography has been published in *British Vogue* and *Harper's Bazaar*. Her work has been displayed around the world consistently for six years. This year she was the cover artist for the Austin International Poetry Festival's anthology, and she was featured in this spring's Schiffer's *Contemporary Wildlife Art*. She is also a published writer and poet.

Todd Camp is an artist who works in multi-media. He is represented in Tulsa by Joseph Gierek Fine Art.

Shoshana Kertesz is a visual artist and poet from Hungary, and she currently lives in West Orange, New Jersey. She studied fine arts in Budapest. Her paintings and photography have been exhibited throughout the Unites States, Hungary, and Israel.

Katherine Minott, M.A., is an artist whose photographic work reflects the Japanese aesthetic of *wabi sabi,* the celebration of things imperfect, impermanent, and incomplete. Her work has appeared in *The Sun, Camas: Nature of the West, New Mexico Magazine, New England Review, Cream City Review,* and *Visual Language Magazine.*

Sarah Sartain is a watercolor artist. In 2004, she won "Best in Show" in Tulsa's Mayfest International Gallery, and she was commissioned to create the official Mayfest poster in 2005. She also painted the official poster for Tulsa's Christmas Parade of Lights in 2009. She is represented in Tulsa by Joseph Gierek Fine Art.

Christopher Woods is a writer, teacher, and photographer who lives in Houston and Chappell Hill, Texas. He has published a novel, *The Dream Patch*; a prose collection, *Under a Riverbed Sky*; and a book of stage monologues for actors, *Heart Speak*. His work has appeared in *The Southern Review, New England Review, New Orleans Review, Columbia,* and *Glimmer Train Stories*, among other publications. His photographs can be seen in his online gallery.

Tina Chang, judge for this year's Pablo Neruda Prize for Poetry, is a poet, teacher, and editor. Born in Oklahoma to Chinese immigrants, she was the first woman to be named Poet Laureate of Brooklyn. She is the author of two poetry collections, *Of Gods and Strangers* and *Half-Lit Houses*, which was a finalist for the 2005 Asian American Literary Award. She has received awards from the New York Foundation for the Arts, Academy of American Poets, and *Poets & Writers*. In 2011, she received The Women of Excellence Award for her outreach and literary impact on the Brooklyn community. Her work has been published in *The New York Times*, *Ploughshares*, and *Asian American Poetry: The Next Generation*.

Karen Russell, judge for this year's Katherine Anne Porter Prize for Fiction, is the author of *Swamplandia!*, *St. Lucy's Home for Girls Raised by Wolves*, and *Vampires in the Lemon Grove: Stories*. She was a 2012 Pulitzer Prize finalist for *Swamplandia!*, and she won the 2012 National Magazine Award for fiction. Russell is a former Fellow of the American Academy of Berlin, and she has taught at Columbia University, Bard College, and the University of Rutgers, Camden, among other universities. She was a 2011 Guggenheim Fellow, and her short stories have appeared in *The New Yorker*, *Granta*, *Zoetrope*, and *Oxford American*.